Instructor's Resource Manual

HUMAN RELATIONS
STRATEGIES FOR SUCCESS

Second Edition

Lowell H. Lamberton, Ph.D.

Leslie Minor-Evans, Ph.D.

Both of
Central Oregon Community College

Glencoe
McGraw-Hill

New York, New York   Columbus, Ohio   Woodland Hills, California   Peoria, Illinois

Glencoe/McGraw-Hill

*A Division of The **McGraw·Hill** Companies*

Microsoft® PowerPoint® is a registered trademark of Microsoft Corporation. ExamView® is a registered trademark of FSCreations, Inc.

Send all inquiries to:

Glencoe/McGraw-Hill
21600 Oxnard Street, Suite 500
Woodland Hills, California 91367-4906

ISBN 0-07-824207-X (Student Edition)
ISBN 0-07-824208-8 (Instructor's Resource Manual)

Printed in the United States of America.

1 2 3 4 5 6 7   026   07 06 05 04 03 02 01

This *Instructor's Resource Manual* for *Human Relations: Strategies for Success,* second edition, was written with you, the instructor, in mind. We hope that it will help you by adding convenience and new ideas to your teaching. Our goal is to make your teaching job easier and more fulfilling, whether you are a first-time instructor or a veteran with years of experience teaching human relations. We include material that will offer teaching suggestions, as well as ideas that you might embellish and improve upon with your own style.

GETTING STARTED

Human relations courses are becoming increasingly popular in both colleges and industry for several sound reasons. The 21st century is experiencing the development of a work environment that includes greater cultural diversity; stronger emphasis on teamwork and group decision-making; and a renewed awareness that sound relationships are at least as important to overall success as the production of quality products and services. More than ever before, effective interpersonal relations form the foundation for good business. Any business education curriculum today must include a human relations component if it is to be timely and meaningful.

This course in business human relations is unique in several ways. Among other features, the course is:

- **Personal**: The topics are directly relevant to the lives of the students.
- **Practical**: Unless course material is applied to the real world of the student, it is only academic and largely useless.
- **Future-oriented**: Most of the skills learned in an effective human relations course must be improved, cultivated, and developed over a period of years. We are never finished learning human relations skills.
- **Necessary:** Often, the students who need this course the most are also the ones who most vigorously resist learning the material. Conversely, the many students who love courses in human relations are often the ones who are already making great progress in this area.

Given the above considerations, an instructor who teaches this course should be prepared for a mixed group of students: students who assume that courses which are subjective and human-oriented are somehow beneath their dignity or level of sophistication; students who are surprised by the course material but are eager to learn; and students who have already discovered some of the more general concepts on their own and want to learn more. From time to time, you will also find working or former managers who are taking the course because someone else wanted them to. Some may be defensive, at least initially.

To be as successful as possible with all of these groups, an instructor should emphasize the relationship between the course material and its application in the workplace. One excellent technique is to draw upon student discussion, as much as possible, for examples of relevant points and for corroboration of principles.

If you are a lecture-oriented instructor, allow and encourage questions during and after your lectures. Using the role-plays and other in-class exercises (e.g., "Working It Out") can aid the learning process and reduce resistance to the material. Even more so than in other courses, students must be involved directly with the course material. Since many of the activities cannot be graded, students need to be internally motivated to learn the precepts and apply them. Your first lecture should be a persuasive one that shows why this material is so crucial to every student's future job and life success. Without exaggerating, you might tell students that this course is the most important course they will ever take. No matter what they intend to do with their lives, they will find that human relations skills can either make them or break them. Anything they can do to improve interpersonal skills will aid in improving their job skills and their personal lives.

TEACHING THE SUBJECT

Through their years of experience, the authors have found that some meaningful generalizations can be made about which classroom methods are the most effective in teaching human relations courses and seminars:

1. **Use a combination of theory and practice.** The principles taught in the textbook are important, and some students will be able to learn them via straight lecture. Keep in mind, though, that this should not be a content course. In a real sense, it is a *skill* course that should resemble Welding 101 more than History 101. Unless experiential exercises are included in your instruction, a percentage of students will have difficulty making the transfer from precept to practice.
2. **Use variety in the classroom.** Students learn in a variety of ways. Besides combining theory and practice, find numerous avenues to pursue both. Lecture, discussion, panel debates, role-plays, and videos are just a few of the methods that you can use effectively.
3. **Establish a relaxed, open atmosphere in the classroom.** Of all subjects, human relations requires an open, real, and relaxed classroom climate. The key to a successful human relations course is often the trust and openness between the instructor and students—and among groups of students. When possible, always try to use a classroom with movable chairs, adjustable lighting, and other features that will create a more comfortable atmosphere.
4. **Be purpose-focused.** Whenever you introduce a new topic, be sure to focus on the real-life purpose of the material. Ask yourself: How will it help the individual student? The workplace? The management process? Profitability?
5. **Listen to the class.** If you haven't already learned this skill, develop the habit of learning from your students. They provide a rich resource of experiences that can often supply better illustrations for human relations concepts than those found in textbooks.
6. **Activate your own creativity.** A human relations course can grow over the years from your own experiments and novel approaches. Don't forget to tap the creativity of your students: Once trust is developed, they can come up with amazingly creative ideas for projects and approaches to the material.

INSTRUCTOR'S RESOURCES—AN OVERVIEW

In each chapter of the *Instructor's Resource Manual,* you will find the following features:
1. **Lecture Outlines** Each chapter has been outlined with an optimum amount of content material for an effective lecture on the topic. We have found that minimal lecture outlines may not be as helpful, especially for the less experienced instructor.
2. **Answers to In-Chapter Questions** Every chapter includes in-depth answers to each photo and figure question found in the Student Edition.

3. **Answers to Review Questions** These answers are based on the experience of many years of author classroom-testing of the book. Forty combined years of classroom teaching in human behavior at various colleges in New England, California, the Midwest, and the Pacific Northwest have also broadened the authors' scope in terms of student reactions and expectations. Whenever possible, we suggest possible student reactions to specific questions. Also, we have attempted to answer the questions with the assumption that some instructors will use selected questions for class discussion; some will use them for homework; and some will do both. Obviously, some questions will foster more lively discussion in the classroom than others.

4. **Suggestions for "Working It Out" Exercises** These exercises vary greatly in content and type. The suggestions offered in the *Instructor's Resource Manual* are based on the authors' own experiences using the exercises in various classroom settings.

5. **Internet Exercises—Tips for Teachers** Correlated to the Student Edition Internet Exercises, these tips provide useful suggestions, questions, and enrichment ideas for you to guide students as they complete these activities.

6. **Answers to Case Studies Questions** Instructors may use the Case Studies for both out-of-class assignments and in-class discussions. Answers are designed to stimulate thought and to provide possible answers in both frameworks.

7. **Additional Activities** At the end of many chapters, the authors have included some additional activities. This assortment includes some exercises that will be useful in the classroom as group role-plays as well as other activities that will lend themselves to individual effort.

Appendices

In this *Instructor's Resource Manual,* two appendices are included at the end of the chapter resource material. The first appendix contains the PowerPoint® Instructor Presentation User's Guide, and the second contains the ExamView Pro® Testbank Generator User's Guide. This material provides important and indispensable information for using the *PowerPoint® Instructor Presentation Software with ExamView Pro® Testbank Generator* CD-ROM that is included with this manual.

SYLLABUS PREPARATION

Complete course scheduling for one full semester and one-quarter semester can be found at the *Human Relations* Instructor's Web site through www.humanrelations.glencoe.com.

Details About the Course

A. Course and section number
B. Course title
C. Required text(s) and supplements
D. Instructor's name and department
E. Office location, phone, and hours

Course Objectives—Example A

This course's objectives are to:

1. Expose students to the most significant human relations issues in today's workplace.
2. Enhance the skills needed to succeed in a workplace that is increasingly based on relationships and customer service.
3. Build an awareness of the overriding importance of healthy self-esteem to anyone in any organization.
4. Create an awareness of the relationship between effective human relations skills and ongoing career success.

Course Objectives—Example B (less formal)

Business human relations emphasizes many practical aspects of human behavior that affect the individual and the group in the workplace. Our goal is to teach skills and procedures, and to raise students' awareness level for the many issues involving relationships on the job. The approach to the material will be as realistic and as directly job-related as possible in a classroom setting. This is also a management course that emphasizes the human relations factors within an organization in terms of management principles.

Grading System

During the term students will have the opportunity to accumulate 500 points:

2 preliminary examinations @ 100 points each	200 points
Final examination @ 150 points	150 points
In-class exercises	50 points
Term project	100 points
Total	**500 points**

Obviously, this suggested grading system can be adjusted to suit the individual instructor's needs and expectations. Some instructors emphasize homework more than exams; some place a great deal of emphasis on in-class work.

DEVELOPING COMPANY TRAINING PROGRAMS

If you are using the textbook in connection with a company training program, you can use the same classroom format without tests and graded exercises. With adult learners, especially those outside of academia, it is often most effective to minimize lecture time and concentrate on in-class skill-building exercises.

Remember that it is illegal to use this material without requiring the company or participants to purchase the book for each student.

CONTENTS

PART THREE: BUILDING YOUR HUMAN RELATIONS SKILLS

APPENDIX 1—POWERPOINT® INSTRUCTOR PRESENTATION USER'S GUIDE

APPENDIX 2—EXAMVIEW PRO® TESTBANK GENERATOR USER'S GUIDE

Chapter 1

Human Relations: A Background

LECTURE OUTLINE

I. **What Is Human Relations?**

II. **The Importance of Human Relations Skills**
   A. Human rights issues
   B. The global marketplace
   C. Growing emphasis on human resources
   D. Renewed emphasis on workgroups
   E. Diversity in the workplace
   F. Human relations and you
      1. You, the manager
      2. You, the entrepreneur
      3. You, the employee

III. **Current Challenges in Human Relations**
   A. Increased competition in the workplace
   B. Dual-career families
   C. Divorce
   D. Two generations of dependents

IV. **A Brief History of Human Relations**
   A. Ancient scenarios
   B. Recent history
      1. Robert Owen
      2. Andrew Ure
      3. Frederick Taylor and **scientific management**
      4. Early abuses of employees
      5. Company towns
      6. Max Weber and **bureaucracy**
   C. History in a timeline
      1. 1920s: The **Hawthorne Experiment**
      2. 1929–1941: The Great Depression
      3. 1941–1945: World War II

4. 1945–1950s: Prosperity and Abraham Maslow
5. Early 1960s: Concepts of **"Theory X"** and **"Theory Y"**
6. Later 1960s: The hippie era
7. 1980s–1990s: Growth of the Quality Movement (**Total Quality Management**)

V. **What Human Relations Is _Not_**
   A. Not a study in how to manipulate others
   B. Not a cure-all for all of your problems
   C. Not "just common sense"

VI. **Areas of Major Emphasis**
   A. **Self-esteem**
   B. **Mutual respect (trust)**
   C. **Self-awareness and self-disclosure**
   D. **Communication skill**
   E. **Group dynamics**
   F. **Motivation**

1.1 Develop Mutual Respect
   1. Develop your self-esteem.
   2. Develop trust.
   3. Cultivate mutual respect.

1.2 Build Your Communication Skills
   1. Learn to communicate honestly and effectively.
   2. Know what you are communicating to others.
   3. Learn to deal effectively with conflict.

PHOTO, page 3: Think about how human relations affect most situations. Can you think of a circumstance that might have been improved by better human relations?

In this circumstance, the older pilot seemed hurried and unreceptive to criticism. This situation would have improved if he had taken the time to listen to the younger pilot's suggestions before taking off, and if he had been more open to criticism. The younger co-pilot seemed to be less assertive than he should have been. Since this was a life-or-death circumstance, he should have spoken out more forcefully regardless of the pilot's attitude.

PHOTO, page 8: What can employers do to help employees in personal crises?

Many employers offer Employee Assistance Programs (EAPs), which offer confidential counseling and other forms of treatment. In addition, some employers also offer benefits, such as health clubs, day care, and personal days, that indirectly combat personal crises.

FIGURE 1.1, page 10: What are the major changes you see in human relations over the years?

Greater respect for employees, including awareness of their needs beyond adequate salary and advancement opportunities, is a primary change. Other changes include switching emphasis from product to process (TQM), analyzing the specific needs of employees and the order of those needs (Maslow), and understanding the impacts of different management styles (McGregor, Theories X and Y).

PHOTO, page 14: Does this problem still exist today?

Sadly, this problem does still exist. Frequency depends on the supply and demand of employees in a particular region, country, or industry.

FIGURE 1.2, page 18: Which of these areas do you personally consider most important to effective human relations?

This depends on your perspective. If you feel that insecurities drive many people to human relations errors, then you may pick "self-esteem"—which, indeed, is considered by many to be one of the most important factors. Other factors will seem just as important, depending on the person and situation.

FIGURE 1.3, page 21: What workplace competencies do you require at your current (or last) job?

This depends on the focus of your job; many jobs require more than one of these competencies. For instance, if your job is to provide technical support, you will need competency not just in Technology skills, but in every other area as well. You will need Resources skills to know how to effectively use your time and allocate funds for new computer equipment when necessary. Also, you will need Interpersonal skills when dealing with end users that need help. Information skills will be essential in troubleshooting problems and reporting them to your department, as well as to end users who are experiencing frustration. Finally, you will also need Systems skills so that you can make appropriate suggestions for ways in which tech support—or a company's computer system—can be improved.

CHAPTER REVIEW, pages 25–29

Review Questions

❶ In your own words, write a one- or two-sentence definition of human relations as you would have defined it before reading this chapter. Then, assuming your definition has changed a bit, write a new one.

Student answers will vary in detail, but should include the skill or ability to work through and with other people, and the desire to understand others. We would hope that the second answer is at least a bit more articulate than the first.

❷ Explain the importance of Elton Mayo and his work in the Hawthorne Studies to the history of human relations.

The Hawthorne Studies changed the way managers looked at employees. As incredible as it now seems, before Mayo's studies managers generally felt that somehow employees weren't really human—that their needs were different from the needs of owners and managers. The authenticity of the Hawthorne Studies has been challenged, but the core findings—right or wrong—have influenced the thinking of several generations of management scholars. Its basic assumptions (such as those about the ego needs of employees and the power of the informal organization) are sound, even though other factors may well have contributed to the behavior of the Hawthorne employees.

❸ How can the development of human relations skills help you on the job as a manager? As an entrepreneur? As an employee?

No other skill is more important to overall career success than human relations. The most common reason for failure in management is inadequacy in this area. After all, a manager works as a leader of people; therefore, nothing could be more important for him or her than people skills. Entrepreneurs need human relations skills for similar reasons, for it is a rare small business that doesn't rely on happy customers for success. Also, an entrepreneur who cannot relate to his or her employees will soon discover the high cost of employee turnover. Most people start their careers as employees working for someone else. Your relationships with fellow employees, bosses, and customers determine to a great extent your success and promotability—as well as your ability to make it on your own.

❹ Explain the role of W. Edwards Deming in the further development of human relations concepts during the past two decades.

Deming started the TQM movement in the U.S. which changed the focus of American companies from an emphasis on product or service to an emphasis on process. This emphasis on process is especially important to human relations because that process includes workplace climate, workplace morale, and the quality of work life. One of Deming's pet peeves was managers who blame their employees for problems they themselves caused. Deming also wanted companies to avoid slogans, numerical goals, and quotas. These devices, he taught, place undue emphasis on the end result, rather than on the enhancement of the process. Use the Internet to learn more about Deming.

❺ List three reasons why human relations issues are more important today than ever before.

Human relations issues are more important today than ever before because of the sweeping societal and technological changes that characterize this part of human history. The high divorce rate, the rise in dual-career families, and the changing service-based economy that seems to be all but eliminating the middle class: All of these factors make human relations a paramount issue. The importance of human relations in our personal and work lives cannot be exaggerated.

❻ Why is self-esteem important to the development of human relation skills?

Self-esteem is the beginning point for all human relations. If you don't like or feel comfortable with yourself, you will inevitably find it difficult to deal comfortably with others. The boss, employee, or entrepreneur with healthy self-esteem will be more accepting of others and will be less jealous, threatened, and intimidated. The manager with healthy self-esteem will be more comfortable managing others without undue expressions of power. On the job, healthy self-esteem is the key to good performance. Chapter 2 deals with this issue in greater depth.

❼ List the six "areas of emphasis" in the study of human relations and explain each one briefly.

1. Self-esteem. See #6, above.
2. Mutual respect. The mutuality is the key issue. Both parties need to respect each other—not always an easy task. Mutual respect involves maturity and the ability to separate your personal feelings from your work life, especially when those feelings involve prejudice and personal dislike.
3. Self-awareness and self-disclosure. Many people go through life with low levels of self-awareness, unaware of the way others perceive them. Self-awareness is the knowledge of how one is being seen and reacted to by others. Self-disclosure involves allowing others to know and understand factors in your life, the clarifying of which will help others relate to you more effectively.
4. Communication skills. Communication involves sending and receiving ideas, thoughts, and feelings. In nearly any human relations problem, miscommunication is at least indirectly involved; thus, the area of communication cannot be stressed too much as an important area of human relations skill development.
5. Group dynamics. Since most of what happens in the workplace today is accomplished through groups, a working knowledge of how groups operate—including pitfalls to avoid—is an extremely important human relations skill.
6. Motivation. Understanding what motivates both yourself and others is a key area of human relations. Don't assume that money is the main motivator. Though it might be for a minority of employees and managers, it is secondary at best for most Americans at the dawn of the 21st century.

8 Why did the human relations movement not make much progress during the Great Depression? Discuss the relevance that experience might have to today's workplace.

During the Great Depression (1929–1941), the shortage of jobs put many managers in the position where they could realistically follow the practice of "firing the problems and hiring the solutions." Sadly, the supply of employees for any given job or occupation still determines the level of humane treatment shown to employees in many companies today.

Critical Thinking Questions

9 Explain the importance of the work of Frederick Taylor and the scientific management movement to the development of modern industry.

As the "father of scientific management," Taylor paved the way for formal study in the field of management practice. Needless to say, courses in management and human relations as they are known today were not offered in Taylor's era; however, the scholars who began the Hawthorne experiment that so piqued Mayo's interest were themselves students of scientific management. Much of the understanding about the interaction between the human factor and productivity has its roots in the scientific management school.

10 What are the problems of today's society that cause greater stress on the job, thus increasing the need for human relations skills? List and explain the importance of each.

1. Increased competition in the workplace. Just a couple of decades ago, a college degree would nearly guarantee at least a starting-level job. Today even MBAs are job hunting. The so-called "baby busters," which are the generations born after 1960, are finding that the job market can be very discouraging.

2. Dual-career families. Most households today need income from both adults to make ends meet. This reality places a strain on both the employee and the workplace—a strain that wasn't there a generation ago.

3. Divorce. The high divorce rate has had devastating impacts on the workplace. The added stress of single parenthood, the stress of the change of lifestyle on the employee, the impact of divorce on self-esteem: all of these factors complicated the workplace of the 21st century for everyone.

4. Two generations of dependents. This relatively new addition to the lifestyle of many has impacts on the workplace that involve stress and added financial needs.

Working It Out

1.1 Communicating With a Supervisor

To the instructor: In most classes, an exhibition-style role-play, which involves only selected members of the class, will be easiest to control. However, if the maturity level of your class is appropriate (and if the class is relatively small), the role-play can work very well with everyone participating.

Whichever method you've chosen, divide class time into three segments—one for positive examples, one for negative ones, and one for evaluation. Allow about 15 minutes for the role-playing and about 20 minutes for evaluation and discussion.

For student playing Doris: In the first session, throw out the principles you have learned in this chapter, and model your firing procedure after the worst boss you can imagine. If you haven't held a job, imagine the worst boss you might ever run into.

In the second session, treat Janet as you yourself would want to be treated in a firing situation. State your case firmly but politely, then listen carefully to whatever objections Janet has.

For student playing Janet: In both sessions, react the way you feel a person like Janet would actually react to being talked to in the way Doris is talking to you. Use your own creativity and acting ability, but listen carefully to whatever Doris tells you, good or bad.

■ INTERNET EXERCISES

Tips for Teachers

These tips will help you, as the instructor, show students how to get the most out of using the Internet for research and education. Although basic tips, they will help the average Internet user understand their online experiences in greater depth.

1. **Research and Evaluate** An important issue for most companies today is the user-friendliness of their Web sites. Ask students to also note the user-friendliness of each company site they visit, then discuss whether this does or does not impact their interest in these companies.

2. **Compare and Contrast** Note to students that most international newspapers and news services are online; two popular examples are *bbc.com* and *indiatimes.com*, and there are hundreds of others. Students can learn priceless information about other cultures, as well as these cultures' perceptions of the U.S. from visiting these sites. In addition, some major search engines (like Yahoo!) also offer foreign sites with services with a news site and links geared toward users in that country or region.

Case Study

1.1 The Fighting Carpenters

1. Which emphasis areas of human relations does this case mostly address?

The most obvious answer is group dynamics; the issue of conflict management falls in this area. There are some problems with group dynamics that should have been taken care of before the situation got this far out of hand. Mutual respect is also involved, as well as communication skill. Alan is going to be forced to call up all of the communication skill he has if he is to solve this problem.

Another relevant issue is the sad reality that nearly every human relations problem in the workplace affects the profitability of the company. You might ask the students if they think the construction company is losing money at this point.

2. What steps should Alan take to solve the conflict in his department?

Since the students haven't covered the chapter on conflict management at this point, their suggestions will likely be based on experience and common sense. Most importantly, Alan needs to get a definition of the problem, then get the members of the two groups to talk to each other. Getting a definition might be difficult because by now the members of the two groups have likely forgotten the original issues. Somewhere in his procedure, he also needs to make clear the consequences of their actions—to the remodeling department, to himself, and to the company.

3. Could Alan have done anything to prevent this problem from occurring in the first place?

More than likely, yes. He should have been aware of the informal work groups in his department, and he should have been listening—listening carefully for the possibility of serious conflicts.

Students who have been working managers will likely say that there might have been no avenue open to Alan to know the hostility was there. In this situation, Alan did already know of tensions, but in some situations a manager will not. For example, the beginnings of the overt hostilities might have taken place away from the job sites.

1.2 The E-Commerce Entrepreneur

1. What should Jenny say to this employee during the talk she has with him?

This case illustrates the importance of human relations skills for a new manager who isn't used to dealing with problems of control. Jenny must keep the customers in mind when talking to Henry. However, she must also communicate in a way so Henry can understand that she isn't trying to cause trouble, but that a real problem exists—and must be solved. Asking questions is often a wise beginning. She could start by asking Henry to put himself in the place of the customer.

If you use this case for class discussion, you can call for a list of possible approaches, then ask the class (or breakout groups) to choose the one that they think would work most effectively. Whatever solution they choose, it should contain the following:

1) A method of preventing (or at least minimizing) defensiveness on the part of Henry.
2) A method of making certain that you will not be losing customers because of this employee's behavior.

2. Should Jenny call a meeting with her entire crew and train them in some of her own selling techniques and human relations policies?

Yes. In fact, she should have trained each employee individually at the outset. However, it's rarely too late to start with such training, and the group approach is probably a good idea. So much of what someone like Jenny encounters seems like "just common sense." That is often the reason such training is often neglected by new entrepreneurs and managers.

3. What procedure could Jenny have followed to prevent these bad experiences from happening?

As mentioned above, a sound training program for Henry and the rest would have been the best beginning point. That training should involve human relations, especially training in communication skills and self-awareness. Also, Jenny could have spent more time with her new employees during their first few days on the job, helping them get acquainted with their duties.

Self-Esteem in Human Relations

LECTURE OUTLINE

I. **What Is Self-Esteem? Self-esteem** is the esteem, or regard, people hold for themselves.
   A. Most people don't like themselves as much as they should.
   B. Most people respond better to persons and situations that are helpful rather than harmful.
   C. Most conceited people are **compensating** for their bad feelings about themselves.

II. **Self-Esteem and Work Performance.** Success in business depends on your level of self-esteem.
   A. If you believe you are good enough to succeed, your chances of success are much better than they would be if you did not hold that belief.
   B. People with **low self-esteem** may experience psychological obstacles (vs. **high self-esteem**).

III. **Types of Self-Esteem.** Your self-esteem will be stronger in one of these areas than in the other.
   A. Self-worth: how you feel about yourself when you are all alone (high or **low self-worth**).
   B. **Self-efficacy:** feelings of confidence in your ability to deal with problems or tasks when they arise.

IV. **Origins of Self-Esteem**
   A. According to Carl Rogers: 1. Parents encourage self-esteem when they provide their children with **unconditional positive regard;** 2. **Conditional positive regard** is love and approval given on the condition that the child meets the parents' needs and expectations.
   B. According to Alfred Adler, feelings of inferiority arise early in life.

V. **What Is Self-Concept?** It is the way you conceive of (or see) yourself.
   A. You base your self-esteem upon your **self-concept.**
   B. Four parts of the self-concept:
      1. **Ideal self:** the vision of your future self
      2. **Looking-glass self:** the self you assume others see
      3. **Self-image:** the way you feel about yourself

   4. **Real self:** you as you really are
   Ideally, all four parts would be one circle.

VI. **Focusing on the Real and Ideal Selves.** Carl Rogers believes that the closer the real and ideal selves are to each other, the happier you will be and the healthier your self-esteem will be.

VII. **Pleasing Yourself and Pleasing Others.** Many people derive purpose from pleasing others, but problems arise when they lose themselves in the process.

2.1 Steps Toward Achieving Higher Self-Esteem
   1. Learn to accept yourself.
   2. Develop an **internal locus of control** (vs. **external**).
   3. Develop a winning skill (for **self-respect**).
   4. Observe and learn from others.
   5. Read biographies.
   6. List your talents.
   7. Stop procrastinating.
   8. Find a **mentor** (or a **role model**).
   9. Avoid surface analysis of yourself and others.
   10. Use **positive self-talk** (for **self-fulfilling prophecy**).
   11. Be aware of the **Pygmalion effect.**
   12. Don't forget the needs of others.

2.2 Steps Toward Combating Low Self-Esteem
   1. Four steps to disarming the **pathological critic:**
      a. Be secure and unafraid.
      b. Be effective and competent in the world.
      c. Be accepted by parents, friends, and significant others.
      d. Have a sense of basic worth and "OK-ness."
   2. Unmask its purpose.
   3. Talk back to the pathological critic.
   4. Make the pathological critic totally useless.
   5. Forgive yourself for not being perfect.

ANSWERS TO IN-CHAPTER QUESTIONS

PHOTO, page 33: How can your opinion of yourself affect your self-esteem? How much does your self-esteem affect the ways that others react to you?

Disliking oneself is an indication of low self-esteem. Your relationships with other people are affected by the way you see yourself. If you tell yourself you are competent and worthy of others' respect, they may see your confidence and treat you accordingly.

PHOTO, page 35: How can you develop high self-esteem in the workplace?

You can tell yourself that you are competent at your job and make a worthwhile contribution to your company. If coworkers and supervisors see that you value yourself as an employee that is worthy of respect, they will treat you that way. Also, you should overcome fears of rejection and vulnerability by sharing constructive thoughts and suggestions openly.

FIGURE 2.1, page 38: How can a parent influence a child's self-esteem?

Parents who show an unconditional positive regard may positively influence their child's self-esteem. Children whose parents show a conditional positive regard may develop low self-esteem.

FIGURE 2.2, page 40: How can you bring your real and ideal selves closer together?

Carl Rogers believes that people need to pay more attention to messages concerning the real self and to adjust the ideal self to reality by making the realistic self a goal.

PHOTO, page 44: What are ways to maintain healthy self-esteem while caring for others' needs?

It is important to not "lose yourself" in the process of caregiving, and to not give so much of your time and energy that you find your own health, needs, and feelings are not being met.

PHOTO, page 47: How can others help you find your talents?

Often, other people notice good qualities in you that you are not even aware of. Ask trusted friends and family members to help you make a list of your talents, and some of their answers will surprise you!

FIGURE 2.3, page 49: Why is it important for affirmations to be as specific as possible?

The more specific affirmations are, the easier it is for you to visualize yourself acting on them. For instance, "I want to do good in this world" is vague and offers you no direction on where to start; however, "I want to donate some of my spare time to the Humane Society" gives you a specific course of action.

PHOTO, page 51: Why does overcompetitiveness prevent healthy self-esteem?

By not allowing others to achieve the same things that you desire, you are preventing yourself from having the trust and comfort level that is necessary for healthy self-esteem to develop.

CHAPTER REVIEW, pages 55–61

Review Questions

❶ Do you ever find yourself compensating for a weakness you feel you have? What behaviors are you compensating for? Do you notice when other people compensate? Describe.

Compensating behaviors are fairly easy to spot in other people. When someone seems to exaggerate the importance of an accomplishment, or is obviously putting disproportionate energy into one part of his or her life while neglecting other parts, you have warning signals.

Identifying such behavior in yourself might be a bit more difficult. When you suspect that one of your behaviors is a compensating behavior, do some self-evaluation.

Ask yourself, "Why am I doing this?" Watch especially for repetitive behaviors. If you keep doing similar things over and over, analyze the reasons why—especially if they are behaviors that serve to make you feel temporarily better about yourself, but are not the best solutions to a long-term problem.

❷ What specific skill or area of your self-concept needs work? Think of some examples of positive self-talk you could use to boost your self-esteem in this area.

Answers will vary. Students may name specific skills related to work or school, interpersonal skills, or personal habits and behaviors. The examples may address general self-concept or specific task-related self-efficacy.

Responses should be only as self-disclosing and personal as the student feels comfortable with.

The self-talk examples should match skills or areas named in the student response. The positive self-talk examples should be stated in the present tense and should be very specific. For example, "I hope to become a better student" is not effective positive self-talk, but "I am a competent student; I read a chapter in my textbook every night" is.

❸ What are the differences among self-concept, self-respect, and self-efficacy? Provide an example of each.

Self-concept is the view you hold of yourself. Although closely tied to self-esteem, it is not the same thing. Self-esteem is based on self-concept, and positive self-concept will encourage high self-esteem.

Self-respect is the degree of respect you hold for yourself. Again, although tied to self-esteem, it is not the same. Self-esteem is also based in part on self-respect. When self-respect is high, so is self-esteem.

Self-efficacy is your feeling of being capable and competent.

Examples will vary. Students may say they view themselves as good students, have high respect for their own academic abilities, and feel competent about completing assignments and taking tests.

❹ Imagine yourself back in the third grade. Your teacher is yelling at you for breaking the chalk while writing on the chalkboard: "Look at what you've done! Go back to your seat!" If you could explain the work of Carl Rogers to your teacher using this example, what would you say?

The teacher is showing **conditional positive regard** by basing his evaluation (or regard) of students on their ability to write on the board without breaking chalk. This is not an effective way to build self-esteem. Since children are very literal, they generalize this incident to mean "I am a bad person in every way because I broke the chalk." A better strategy for the teacher is to use **unconditional positive regard**, in which he tells the child that a particular behavior is not acceptable but also lets the child know that he or she is still a person worthy of respect and acceptance. The teacher might say something like, "Thank you for showing us the arithmetic problem on the board. Please hold the chalk a little more gently so it doesn't break next time. That way, we can all have a turn at the board."

❺ Which would you rather have in your current job or profession, a mentor or a role model? If you were mentoring a new employee in your field, what kinds of things would you say and do?

A **mentor** is someone who has been in the position you are now in, and a role model is someone you can look to for guidance who has not necessarily been in your current situation. You may not even have active interaction with a role model. A mentor is mostly a teacher, while the mentee (you, in this case) is mostly a learner.

Most people say they would rather have a mentor because there is more chance for guidance and direction. A mentor is not always available, though, and you may run the risk of taking on too much of the mentor's identity (including his or her shortcomings) during the mentoring process.

❻ Two employees who are learning a new accounting system are talking about it. "It's no use," says the first. "Management is always dumping these new things on me that I can't learn." The second one replies, "We can learn this; it will just take a little practice. Come on, let's try it." According to Rotter, which employee has an internal locus of control, and which employee has an external locus of control? How will this likely affect each one's ability to learn the new system?

The first employee has an external locus of control, and is more likely to feel helpless, hopeless, and incompetent. He likely feels that the world is happening to him, instead of feeling that he is an active part of the decision-making going on around him in the world. The second employee has an internal locus of control; he is more likely to feel competent, will be more likely to ask for help in order to understand the new system, and will probably learn sooner, with fewer problems in the process.

❼ You are certain that your coworkers see you as a cranky, reclusive hermit. Actually, they think of you as a shy person who is quiet but nice to be around. How can this difference between self-concept and others' opinions exist side-by-side regarding the same person?

This type of perception problem means that your looking-glass self is out of focus. You need to gain input from the people you work with so that your looking-glass self can better reflect reality.

❽ You are waiting for your appointment for an important job interview. A voice inside you shouts, "You're so stupid, fat, and ugly! You'll never get this job!" Who is this voice? Why is it sending you these messages? What will you do to stop it?

This internal voice belongs to the **pathological critic**.

The pathological critic knows that you need to feel secure, competent, and accepted; it knows that you need to feel a sense of basic self-worth. The pathological critic generally tries to hurt you by damaging your self-esteem. Its motives vary greatly; for instance, it may be trying to make you feel bad now, as a way of reducing the pain of rejection later in case you do not get the job.

To stop the pathological critic, talk back to it. Tell it you are a good job candidate and you know it's lying to you. Take a deep breath and do the best you can on your interview.

Critical Thinking Questions

9 Is an internal locus of control good to have in *all* situations? Can you think of a situation in which it would *not* be helpful to feel in complete control of your life? For example, when something truly terrible happens, such as a natural disaster or other tragedy, are you really in control of events? If you are not in control of events, what are you in control of in such a situation?

Answers will vary. The best answers will explain that even when people are not in control of actual events, they are still in control of their responses to them. Another important point is that it is not helpful or healthy to assume responsibility for events beyond your control. Many people expend energy and time in thinking, "If only I had/had not done something, this might not have happened." It is better to assume an external locus of control for events that are truly out of your control.

10 Some people say that when they were children, their parents lacked confidence in them and treated them with conditional (instead of unconditional) positive regard—and this treatment, rather than reducing their self-esteem, challenged them to work harder and succeed. Do you agree that such treatment, then, might be *good* instead of damaging to people's developing self-esteem? Explain.

Answers will vary. Some students will say that they were motivated by others' low expectations of them. These people may fit the profile of the hardy or resilient person, which is introduced in Chapter 14. The hardy person sees problems as challenges to overcome, is committed to reaching a goal, and feels a strong internal locus of control. For most people, however, poor treatment by parents and important others is damaging to self-esteem.

Working It Out

2.1 Exploring Your Self-Esteem

This scale can be used as an in-class activity or short homework assignment. Some students may be reluctant to discuss their self-esteem scores in class, but may find it less threatening to talk about some of the items as indicators of self-esteem.

Working It Out

2.2 Testing Your Locus of Control

This scale is brief enough so that instructors can use it as an in-class activity. Students usually respond favorably to this activity. The instructor should be prepared to restate for students the advantages of the internal versus external locus of control.

■ INTERNET EXERCISES

Tips for Teachers

1. **Self-Assessment** Unfortunately, dead links are sometimes unavoidable, even with well-established sites. As the instructor, try to test each link before assigning it. If you find any dead links, as is sometimes unavoidable, ask students to go to the site's main page and try to find substitute material. Often, what appears to be a dead link is just a link that has been updated, then moved or renamed in some way.

2. **Research and Write** Certain pages offer a greater variety of resources than a single exercise can reveal, and you can encourage students to explore more than the specific pages assigned. Try offering extra credit for site analyses, either through stand-alone assignments or additional questions on tests.

2.1 Good Enough for CAD?

1. Where is this voice inside Ian's head coming from? If you were Ian, what would you say to this voice?

This is the pathological critic attacking Ian for not being perfect, and reminding him about all the "shoulds" he had heard from his family while growing up. Ian should tell this inner critic, "Stop!" Ian should talk back to the voice, telling it (himself) that he has done well in the classes, is seeking a job that interests him, and should apply for that job.

2. Do you think that Ian has a self-esteem problem? If so, what were the origins of the problem?

It sounds like Ian has a definite self-esteem problem, and the origins are the same origins that are often cited: parents and family members making children feel lowered self-worth, either by treating them with conditional positive regard, or, as in this case, by making them feel inferior. Telling Ian he was "the dumb one" reduced his self-efficacy, self-respect, and self-esteem.

3. Imagine yourself as Ian's supervisor. If you found out about Ian's classes and his dreams of going into design, what would you say to him?

A good manager would tell Ian to go for it! Employers, for the most part, know that employees are more productive when they are doing the jobs they want to be doing. Many companies encourage their employees to take classes and improve their skills, and are even willing to reimburse those who do so. If Ian were to check into his employee benefits, he might find that his company is not only willing to hire him into this job, but is also willing to pay for classes to upgrade his skills.

2.2 How About a Mentor?

1. What do you imagine Jylisa is preparing to say? What should she say?

Jylisa may be preparing to say; "Thanks, but no thanks." She also may be preparing to say; "Well, you're not really what I had in mind as a mentor."

What she *should* say is: "Kevin, that's a wonderful idea. Let's talk about it." Kevin sees himself as having been in her place, and in many ways he probably has. He may have felt left out due to his ethnicity, and senses that Jylisa feels left out too. If he is willing to help her along in her career, she should take advantage of the knowledge he has to teach her.

2. What is the function of a mentor? What do you see as the roles that Kevin and Jylisa might take, if Kevin were able to be Jylisa's mentor?

A mentor is an informal teacher who has been in the place of the employee. The mentee (the person being mentored) is the informal student.

Kevin's role as a mentor would be to give Jylisa advice on her job performance and the politics of their workplace, in order to enhance her job performance and help her feel that she is an integral part of the company.

3. Would Jylisa be better off with a mentor or with a role model? Why? What specific advantages to Jylisa's self-esteem do you see possible in this situation?

Jylisa would probably be better off with a mentor because she feels left out and does not know how to fit in with this group. A role model would not be able to give her specific advice on how to fit in with this company.

Kevin's obvious confidence in Jylisa's abilities is a good start toward building her self-esteem. Jylisa sounds as if she is not completely comfortable with Kevin, but he can still become a helpful and trusted mentor to her. In anecdotal reports, many women have said that it's hard to find a good mentor to help them get to top management levels since people in these positions are more likely to be men. This should not stop them, or Jylisa in this example, from getting advice and guidance from anyone who is willing to take on the role.

ADDITIONAL ACTIVITY

Water-Cooler Wit Role-Play

Purpose: To awaken awareness to the defensiveness people often exhibit, based on low self-esteem and fear.

The Case: Sam is walking down the corridor in his company during the morning break. This is his first real job since completing college, and he wants to make a good impression. He sidles up to a group of about six other employees, most of whom he knows. He says something that he thinks is very witty. The response from the others, though, is negative. They look at him as if to ask, "Where did this loser come from?" Sam has several choices in terms of the reaction he is going to express. He can *retreat*, *attack*, plan to *compensate* in some way, *rationalize* what has just happened, *engage* in fantasy and imagine getting even with them using some superior powers—*or* he can calmly accept the fact that he probably said something inappropriate and then go on, attempting to become a part of the group of employees without letting the initial rejection damage his self-esteem.

Procedure: This role-play works best as an exhibition exercise. In other words, a group of six or seven will be selected from the class to perform the role-play for the rest of the class members. Be careful in the selection procedure, especially for the student who plays Sam. Let the student volunteers have some time to write their scripts and plan their strategy. Often, it is most effective to give them a couple of days to get together outside of class. As the exercise begins, they should role-play at least three defensive and non-constructive scripts that Sam could play out—with different members playing Sam each time, if they like.

After the entire exercise is played out, ask the rest of the class for their input. Of the defensive scripts, ask these questions:

1. Which role-play was the most effective for Sam? Why?
2. Which role-play was the most effective for the others in the group? Why?
3. Which role-play was the most destructive to Sam? Why?
4. Which role-play was the most destructive to the others in the group? Why?
5. Why is the non-defensive approach best?

This exercise can produce a great deal of positive discussion. After all, everyone remembers an incident of saying something they later regretted. Often the discussion is the most productive part of the entire exercise.

If you have time, you might assign two or more groups to work independently, ending with a series of these presentations rather than just one. In that case, your class can also discuss the differences in the individual presentation. Depending on your own classroom style, you might want to use this role-play participatively; that is, you can get the entire class involved by dividing into several groups in class, playing the roles simultaneously.

Self-Awareness and Self-Disclosure

LECTURE OUTLINE

I. **Self-Awareness** is the ability to see yourself realistically, without a great deal of difference between what you are and how you assume others see you.
   A. It can be seen as getting an accurate *looking-glass self*.
   B. Most people have blind spots in their own self-awareness.

II. **Barriers to Effective Human Relations**
   A. Building walls: Many people spend much of their lives unknowingly building walls to keep others from seeing who they really are and what they really think.
   B. Many people believe if these walls are removed, others may not like them or they will be swept away by a violent release of repressed feelings.
   C. Effective removal of these walls is part of becoming fully human.
   D. Author Marie Lindquist believes that people often hold back the truth about themselves out of fear of appearing incomplete. This feeling of incompleteness can, however, also be positive motivation to grow and develop emotionally.

III. **The Johari Window**
   A. The **open pane** contains information that you know about yourself and have no reason to hide from others.
   B. The **hidden pane** contains information and feelings that you are hiding from other people.
   C. The **blind pane** contains everything other people can see about you, but you can't see yourself.
   D. The **unknown pane** is the area that nobody—including yourself, your dearest friends, or your family—can see. In this area, you may **repress**, or block off memories that cause pain, embarassment, or guilt.

IV. **Self-Disclosure** is letting another person know your real thoughts and feelings: "Only as we are open and honest with ourselves can we really know ourselves."
   A. Reasons to withhold the truth. Often you have legitimate reasons for withholding the truth, such as the need to get along with others, get them to like you, or protect others' feelings.
   B. Most reasons are *not* valid! They generally include the need to feel all-powerful, perfect, superior, in control, approved of, or safe from others who will challenge you; denial that you have problems; or attempts to mask feelings of inadequacy.
   C. Most people adapt their behaviors to their audience. If you self-disclose, others will generally follow. If you choose not to self-disclose, others will be unlikely to do so.
   D. Learned behaviors. As children, you may have learned that emotions should be hidden from others. These feelings are then held within the hidden pane.

V. **Failure to Self-Disclose**
   A. Keeping secrets from others fosters paranoia and makes it impossible to have an honest and open relationship. Common occurrences when failing to self-disclose include:
      1. loss of relationships with others.
      2. slowdown of personal growth.
      3. waste of time and energy.
      4. loss of sense of identity.

VI. **Levels of Disclosure**
   A. John Powell has divided self-disclosure into **five levels of communication**.
      1. Level 5: **Cliché conversation** is generic small talk, such as *What's happening, How ya' doin'?* or *How's the weather up there today?* **Nonconversation** is a way of describing this type of communication.
      2. Level 4: Reporting facts about others is conversation about others only, such as coworkers; therefore, no real self-disclosure takes place yet.
      3. Level 3: Expressing **ideas and judgments** is similar to testing the water before jumping in it. This level is usually self-censored, but some low-level risks are taken here.

4. Level 2: Expressing feelings and emotions. If others are to understand who you really are, Powell says that "you must tell someone what's in your gut as well as what's in your head." This is **gut level communication**.

5. Level 1: **Peak communication** is taken from Maslow's concept of the *peak experience*. Powell states that peak experiences will not happen often; when they do, those involved may feel an almost perfect and mutual empathy.

B. A key to improved human relations: Level 2. In Level 2, gut-level communication creates an atmosphere where human relations can grow, people can understand themselves better, and conflict will be reduced. In an organization, such benefits translate into greater efficiency and productivity.

C. Important quotation from Powell: "I will understand only as much of myself as I have been willing to communicate to another." On Level 2:

1. genuine emotions and points of view are shared, giving each person a greater sense of identity.
2. people can grow toward maturity.
3. genuine communication brings out honesty in others.

VII. The Risk Factor

A. Self-disclosure involves risks.

B. Some common fears involving self-disclosure include fear of losing control, becoming trapped in some way, learning something about yourself you really don't want to know, losing respect, looking like a loser, being belittled, being rejected, or falling under the control of others.

3.1 Know When to Stop. It is important to understand some boundaries when self-disclosing.

1. Self-disclosing might seem difficult, and you can easily take the idea too far and disclose too much.

2. A good general rule of thumb is to avoid discussing personal matters with strangers or at the workplace.

3.2 Pay Attention to Differences. Cultural climates are important to consider. Gender, ethnic groups, social position, and geographic regions are factors within cultural climates.

1. Knowing how much to disclose and how fast often depends on many factors, including the specific circumstances and situation.

2. You can minimize your uncertainty by allowing the other person to take the lead.

3. Important factors include gender, race, and social position.

4. A more individual factor is the level of openness of the person with whom you are speaking regardless of that person's position, background, or location.

3.3 Facing Fear

1. Dale Carnegie gives three suggestions for moving ahead even when fear is present:
   a. Imagine the **worst possible scenario.**
   b. Prepare yourself to accept this scenario.
   c. Proceed with a plan.

2. Not all people will like your self-disclosure, so plan on that!
   a. If everyone liked you, you would be a rare person indeed.
   b. Turn criticism into a positive force: Ask yourself how you might improve from this.
   c. You don't need to be perfect; in fact, worrying about this might be one of the reasons you were not self-disclosing to begin with.

ANSWERS TO IN-CHAPTER QUESTIONS

PHOTO, page 65: Do you know anyone like Betsy, who can't understand why others fail to read her feelings, or like Mona, who isn't receiving messages that other people are convinced they are sending?

Student answers will vary, but Betsy's and Mona's communication problems have to do with self-awareness and self-disclosure. If Betsy could communicate her needs clearly, she could be reasonably confident that her message was understood.

FIGURE 3.1, page 68: Does everyone have all four of these "panes" of perception?

We all have these four panes, but each window reveals different ways in which we interact with others.

FIGURE 3.2, page 69: How does the open pane expand?

The open pane expands in relationships where you disclose more of yourself to someone you trust and become more self-aware in the process.

FIGURE 3.3, page 73: How can your identity be affected when you refuse to self-disclose?

When you refuse to self-disclose you aren't able to retain a sense of who you are.

PHOTO, page 75: What did Tyrone's sister do when he was reluctant to self-disclose?

She used gentle persistence, combined with a foundation of trust and a willingness to listen. This helped Tyrone feel comfortable enough to self-disclose.

PHOTO, page 76: What kind of self-disclosure is inappropriate during an interview?

Disclosing personal matters during an interview is inappropriate. Often watching the other person's signals and letting them take the lead help make things flow smoothly.

FIGURE 3.4, page 77: On which level do you feel you are having "real" conversation and disclosure?

Most people would say that Level 2 is the most "real" in terms of communication and disclosure.

PHOTO, page 87: What was Lin Jin's first step when she planned to confront Bruce?

She tried to determine the *worst case scenario*, then planned how she would handle it. This gave her the confidence that, whatever the outcome, she was prepared.

CHAPTER REVIEW, pages 89–94

Review Questions

❶ **What does the term "self-awareness" mean to you after reading this chapter? Use an illustration from your own experience to clarify your definition.**

Actual wording will vary, but students' definitions should include something about the ability to see themselves realistically. It should also stress that any variation between what they and others see should at least be logically explainable.

Personal life examples could include anything observed in others or in the students themselves that shows very high or low self-awareness.

❷ **Why do people often withhold from others their true selves—or parts of who they really are? Have you ever withheld your true feelings? If so, explain why.**

The simplest answer is fear—fear of being discovered. People want to feel all-powerful, perfect, superior—anything but what they honestly are. Another issue is control: People want to control others' reactions to, and opinions of, them. Still another is denial, when people want to deny that they have problems. Finally, low self-esteem is a large factor. People with low self-esteem feel inadequate, unlovable, and otherwise unworthy.

The last part of the question is subjective and personal, so answers will vary. If a student claims to never have withheld true feelings, he or she is likely lying, has either low self-awareness or a bad memory, or is excessively extraverted.

❸ **How can a lack of appropriate self-disclosure be a barrier to effective relations with others? Specifically, how can a failure to disclose affect your position in the workplace?**

Whenever you play a role, your real self is likely to get buried. For example, many managers feel they can't show who they really are because they have to act the part of a boss. For all of the reasons listed in the textbook, they are less than happy and less effective as managers because they are not being themselves. Conversely, many employees fall into a similar trap because they feel than can't really be themselves around their immediate supervisor. Other workplace applications can certainly be made.

4 **Briefly explain each of the four panes of the Johari Window. How can this model help you understand yourself better by understanding your relationships with others?**

   A. **The open pane** contains information that you know about yourself and have no reason to hide from most other people. It will become larger as you progress in a relationship with someone else. For example, as a friendship develops, you will likely show more and more of yourself to the other person, until the pane begins to look like the one in Figure 3.2.

   B. **The hidden pane** contains information and feelings that you are hiding from other people. It might be information that you feel is simply nobody else's business, or data that you are ashamed or afraid to share with others.

   C. **The blind pane** contains everything other people can see about you, but you cannot see yourself. As a relationship develops, this pane will tend to grow smaller, as a caring friend allows you to see more and more into your blind areas.

   D. **The unknown pane** is both exciting and frightening because it deals with areas that nobody, even you, can see. It could include an undeveloped talent or ability, heroism, or criminality. Feedback from the right person can trigger information that has long remained unexamined.

The Johari window helps people to examine themselves in terms of how much information about themselves they know, show, and withhold from others. If nothing else, the Johari Window should allow you to do some serious self-examination in terms of your willingness to disclose who you really are and what circumstances are comfortable to you.

5 **Think of an incident in your life when someone over-disclosed to you or someone else. How did the incident affect the relationship? What steps can you take to avoid overdisclosing?**

Virtually all students will be able to recall such an incident from their own lives. Typically, some sort of strain was placed on the relationship. A related discussion question that you as the instructor might ask is: "What factors specifically made you feel that overdisclosure was taking place?"

Overdisclosing tends to overwhelm the listener with information that violates the listener's comfort zone. The results are embarrassment and a decreased likelihood of meaningful conversation with the listener in the future.

To avoid overdisclosing, one must constantly check the other person's area of comfort. The subtle messages the other person sends about what areas he or she is comfortable discussing usually indicate the area of safety expected from you. One should also be aware of cultural differences that determine acceptable levels of self-disclosure.

6 **How might self-disclosure help you in your relationship with your manager? With coworkers? Can you think of examples that illustrate either negative or positive effects of self-disclosure in the workplace?**

First, self-disclosure is letting others know what is really going on inside you—in terms of your feelings, thoughts, and desires. Many people hide a great deal of their true selves from those they work with and for. Whenever the real person emerges, relationships are likely to be more genuine. They might not always be better, but they will be based more on reality. More often than not, human relations will improve with just the right amount of self-disclosure. When a manager catches a glimpse of your real self, it will be more difficult in many cases for him or her to dehumanize you; you will become more real to the manager. The same is true with coworkers.

Students often have a good time with the second part of the question. Some students will remember an incident in their workplace where over-disclosing wasn't really the issue, but perhaps otherwise appropriate self-disclosure somehow backfired on the discloser. Such incidents can provide fodder for in-depth discussions as to what factors were in place that allowed the negative consequences to take place.

7 **Of John Powell's five levels of communication, what is the best one for everyday use? Explain why.**

Level 2, the "gut level," is the best everyday level. Students sometimes ask why it isn't more logical to choose Level 1. The reason is that Level 1 is peak communication, a communication level you achieve infrequently, if ever. From such peak experiences, you can learn a great deal about yourself and others; however, one should not expect such a level to become an everyday occurrence.

Beyond that, Level 2 is real, honest, and forthright. It contains no game-playing or cover-ups. The key is that you let the other person know what is in your gut, not merely what is in your mind. When people communicate on this level, human relationships grow, people understand themselves better, and conflict is reduced. As the text points out, this openness improves relationships, allows people to mature, and brings out the honesty in others.

8 **Discuss Dale Carnegie's three rules for reducing fear. Would any of them work for you when self-disclosure is the issue? Why or why not?**

Carnegie's three rules involve moving ahead with things even when fear is present, using the worst possible scenario approach.

A. Start with the **worst possible scenario:** Imagine the very worst thing that could happen as a result of whatever is bothering you. Then remind yourself that the worst is usually unlikely to happen.

B. Prepare yourself psychologically to accept and live with this worst possible outcome, should it happen. Become ready for whatever might happen in that context.

C. Proceed with a plan. Plan for the worst possible scenario as though it would actually happen, then plan adaptations for the more likely and less threatening outcomes that will probably happen.

If you use this question for class discussion, you might run into students who claim that they've tried this approach without success. Lead the discussion around to reasons why the failure might have occurred. Was the plan not followed as Carnegie suggested? Was a step missed? Make them do the thinking and help them draw the conclusions.

Critical Thinking Questions

❾ **Have you ever experienced differences in people's level of self-disclosure based on where they live (in another country or part of your country, for example)? What did you observe, if anything?**

Students who like personal application questions will usually respond well to this one, especially those who have traveled extensively. Usually, some students will observe great differences in different geographical locations. However, be prepared for disagreements about what one really finds in other areas.

If you are using this question for class discussion, try to get to the bottom of such disagreements; often, they are based on perception, not hard fact.

❿ **Are you as self-aware as you would like to be? If not, what steps can you take to allow yourself to reach a higher level of self-awareness?**

Answers will vary. After having read the chapter, some students will perceive a lack of self-awareness in themselves, but will feel helpless as to how to improve.

The best advice is for such students to begin tuning in to others' reactions to them. Another exercise that often helps is to practice putting themselves in the other person's listening position. Students should ask, "What might I sound like, look like, and come off like to this person?" Self-awareness is a skill that is best developed while learning to interact with others.

■ INTERNET EXERCISES

Tips for Teachers

1. **Read and Write** For students who do not have Internet access at home, suggest free alternatives, such as the school's computer center or any public library. Some coffeehouses also offer Internet access for a fee.

2. **Self-Assessment** Encourage students to compare this textbook's coverage of various subjects with the coverage found on assigned Web sites. How are they different? How do these different approaches contribute to the students' learning? Do they raise any questions?

Working It Out

3.1 The "Opener Scale" Questionnaire

This scale measures students' perception of their ability to get others to open up. The items measure student perceptions of others' reactions to them, their interest in listening, and their interpersonal skills. Use class discussion to determine the significance of differences in scoring.

For best results, the questionnaire should be administered during class time. If time doesn't permit, send it home with some type of "hook" to make sure they do it—points, responsibility to the group—whatever works with the makeup and maturity level of the class.

Working It Out

3.2 Your Feelings About Self-Disclosure

This exercise is quite personal and is thus likely to be threatening to many students. Using this as a group exercise would be recommended only in a small, mature class where close relationships have already developed—which would be an unusual class.

The final summary questions could be used for class discussion, even if you have only a small percentage of the students who would be willing to share them. Often, one student's self-disclosure will stimulate another student who was previously reticent to talk. After all, self-disclosure is the chapter topic; some practice in the art would be valuable, as long as it doesn't get out of hand. You, as the instructor, must use judgment and discretion to make the exercise successful.

3.1 Anthony's Confrontation

1. How did self-disclosure help the problem in this case?

As in so many instances in life, this case shows two people who have distorted perceptions of each other. Anthony sees only what his perceptions allow him to see and what Youngberg discloses to him. When his open area enlarges, so does Youngberg's. If either one is willing to establish a more communicative relationship, the open pane should enlarge even further. Given this specific situation, it is unlikely that any progress would have been made without the self-disclosure (minimal though it really was) that the two were willing to share.

2. Was Mr. Youngberg doing anything wrong? If so, what?

Of course he was. A manager should learn to know his or her employees and treat them fairly, even if one has a bad attitude. Also, if he felt that Anthony's behavior showed a negative attitude, he should have initiated a talk with him quite a while before the action in this case. To ignore such problems is counterproductive and bad for overall morale.

3. How could the problem of unfair targets have been avoided?

The targets should have been set impersonally in a standardized manner to avoid any suspicions of favoritism or discrimination. Ideally, they would have been set with at least some employee input, using industry standards as beginning benchmarks.

3.2 The Angry Computer Technician

1. How self-aware is Harry? On what do you base your assessment?

Harry could be more self-aware. Based on the case, he likely thinks of himself as a nice guy. However, he seems to be less in touch with the feelings that accompany the "nice guy" image. He apparently resents people who "take advantage of nice guys." More importantly, he doesn't seem to be in touch with the intensity of those feelings within himself. When they do come out, the feelings surprise others, such as Sam. Perhaps they even surprise Harry.

2. How could self-disclosure have prevented this confrontation? How could it help now? Has it helped in some way already?

Harry's self-awareness level has damaged his ability to self-disclose. Assuming that Harry was in touch with his own feelings of being used, he could have told Sam over one of their many lunches together that he is bothered when people take advantage of his being good-natured.

It could help now if Harry would only take the time to sit down and share with Sam his true feelings about the incident and the issues that preceded it. If Sam asks the right questions, Harry might be forced into seeing, and hopefully admitting, some of the mistakes he has made in the past.

Sam's attitude shows that the self-disclosure which has taken place, though swift and brutal, has helped him readjust his assumptions about Harry and what he stands for.

3. What else might you do if you were Sam?

Student responses will vary. Many students will likely suggest that Sam should start picking Harry's brain once Harry has cooled down. The more real, honest data Sam can get from Harry, the better his chances are of becoming a closer friend and exchanging genuine self-disclosure. For one thing, he should become a careful watcher and listener. He especially should be looking for nonverbal signals that give away Harry's true feelings about other issues in their dealings with one another. Some students have suggested that this incident could be a turning point in Sam and Harry's working relationship. What Sam does during the next few days can determine whether that turning point will be negative or positive.

Attitudes

Chapter 4

LECTURE OUTLINE

I. What Is an Attidute?
   A. **Attitudes** are your evaluations of people, ideas, issues, situations, or objects.
   B. Attitudes result from beliefs and feelings people have about themselves and others; they affect the way people treat each other.
   C. Attitudes consist of thoughts, feelings, and actions.
   D. Some attitudes are based on low self-esteem developed during childhood.

II. What Makes a Good Attitude? Dr. David Myers lists four ingredients for a happy or **positive attitude**:
   A. Healthy self-esteem. Strategies that improve self-esteem will improve attitudes.
   B. Optimism. Happy people have hope for the future. Optimistic people are not only happier than pessimistic people, but are healthier.
   C. **Extraversion.** Happy people are outgoing.
   D. **Personal control.** Happy people feel a sense of personal control over their lives.

III. Changing Attitudes
   A. To change attitudes, people need **feedback**, or information about how they are performing.
   B. In giving feedback, deal with facts not opinions.

IV. Positive Attitudes and Optimal Experiences
   A. Dr. Csikszentmihalyi defines **flow** or **optimal experience** as the feeling of being engaged and absorbed in an activity that truly makes you happy.
   B. Activities that lead to flow experiences are challenging, require a specific skill, are absorbing, have clear goals, provide feedback, require complete concentration, allow sense of personal control, lead to loss of self-awareness and sense of time.

V. "Flow" in Our Everyday Lives. Finding flow in your work is a key to happiness.

VI. Attitudes and Job Satisfaction
   A. Job performance leads to job satisfaction.
   B. Employees who are satisfied with their jobs are absent less often and have higher job performance.

VII. Positive Attitudes and Managers: Theory X and Theory Y
   A. Many managers hold **Theory X** assumptions:
      1. Most people don't want to work or enjoy working.
      2. Most people must be bribed, controlled, threatened, or directed to work.
      3. Most people prefer to be directed, to avoid responsibility, and have security above all.
   B. **Theory Y** managers hold more positive beliefs:
      1. Work is as satisfying as play or rest.
      2. Employees can direct themselves.
      3. People will work for rewards.
      4. Most people will seek and accept responsibility.
      5. Many people are creative and imaginative, and these mental abilities are often underutilized.
   C. When changing from Theory X to Theory Y management, managers should consider the maturity level of the employees, the meaningfulness of the work, and the speed of the transition.

4.1 Changing Pessimism to Optimism. Dr. Martin Seligman describes a process for changing pessimism to optimism:
   1. When facing a catastrophe, think of the worst thing that could happen and what could prevent it.
   2. Now think of the best thing that could happen and how to make that happen.
   3. Finally, think of the most likely thing that will happen and how you will manage it if it happens.

4.2 Building Positive Attitudes
   1. As much as possible, be positive.
   2. Don't get trapped in others' negative attitudes.
   3. Look for good qualities in yourself, others, and your organization.
   4. Don't let outside situations push you around.
   5. Become goal-oriented.

ANSWERS TO IN-CHAPTER QUESTIONS

PHOTO, page 97: Do you overreact to certain events or situations? What do you think are the reasons behind it?

If you overreact to some situations, you can look at several things, including your level of self-esteem, your overall optimism and ability to "bounce back" after setbacks, and your willingness to see the best in any situation.

PHOTO, page 101: How does your attitude positively affect your current job?

Your answer will reflect any or all of the traits described above; the exact combination will depend on the individual.

PHOTO, page 102: Is your locus of control internal or external? How can you change an external locus of control?

You can change an external locus of control by accepting responsibility for your attitudes, moods, and life choices.

FIGURE 4.1, page 103: How optimistic are you?

Your answer may depend on how you score on this test, as well as on your own self-concept. If you feel that you are not optimistic enough, ask yourself how you can begin to shift your focus and develop an attitude that is more focused on solving problems—and reaching goals.

PHOTO, page 105: Do you feel "flow" at your job? What makes you feel "flow"?

You feel flow when you do the type of challenging, creative work that you enjoy most. Flow can occur while you are working, playing, or pursuing a hobby, but it actually happens most while people are at work.

FIGURE 4.2, page 108: What are some ways that you can give constructive feedback?

Some options are:

Be sure to deal with facts rather than opinions and descriptions rather than judgments.

Try to strike a balance between negative and positive feedback. Some authorities on this subject suggest giving two positive messages for every negative one.

You can probably think of many others.

PHOTO, page 111: What work environment would be best for a Theory Y manager? For a Theory X manager?

Theory Y managers can thrive anywhere in which employees are mature, interested in their work, and motivated enough to appreciate long-term goals. Theory X managers are probably better for environments where employees are immature, the work is uninteresting, or there is no sense of long-term accomplishment because of the repetitiveness of the task (such as assembly-line work).

FIGURE 4.3, page 112: What factors determine whether Theory X or Theory Y management is best for your company?

Three key factors should be considered:

1. The maturity level of the employees
2. The meaningfulness of the work
3. The speed of the transition

FIGURE 4.4, page 112: Can a Theory X manager succeed even when he or she knows that employees strongly dislike their jobs?

Yes, but it depends on the situation. For instance, the benevolent Theory X manager will compensate for an unpleasant work environment with rewards such as high salary, frequent praise, and other perks that will help make the job more bearable for employees.

Review Questions

❶ How are attitudes related to self-esteem? How does a change in one affect the other?

People with low self-esteem often have negative attitudes that are based more on their own feelings of inadequacy than on reality. They will often be unable to perceive reality as others do because their perception is clouded by a low self-concept. Your self-perception also colors the perceptions that others have of you: If you don't like yourself very well, others won't like you either. Low self-esteem is, in effect, an attitude you hold toward yourself.

Changing one's attitude for the worse changes self-esteem for the worse, creating a downward spiral. In contrast, changing one's attitude for the better raises self-esteem.

❷ Where do attitudes come from? When in people's lives do they develop?

Attitudes based on low self-esteem develop early in childhood, when parents consciously and unconsciously transmit their own attitudes to their children.

As discussed in Chapter 2, when parents treat their children with unconditional positive regard, healthier attitudes based on positive self-esteem are likely to develop. When parents treat children with conditional positive regard, low self-esteem is the likely result.

Attitudes continue to develop throughout people's lives. When attitudes continue to be based on low self-esteem, they affect even seemingly unrelated facets of life.

❸ How do positive attitudes affect the workplace? How can negative attitudes hurt the success of a business?

Positive attitudes are often passed around among coworkers. Employees with positive attitudes are generally more satisfied at work, are absent less often, and are more likely to look for solutions when problems arise.

Negative attitudes are expensive in more ways than one. They cost the business money in lost productivity, lowered morale, and possibly lost customers. They can also be contagious among coworkers. Since job satisfaction and job performance are linked, attitudes on the job are important to the overall success of a business.

❹ Explain the statement, "Happy people control their own destinies."

Students will have different responses based on their own personal experiences. Most important is understanding that happiness can be a choice, rather than a state of mind that comes and goes at the whim of fate. If you can control your happiness level, you are likely to control many other facets of your own life, and your happy attitude will undoubtedly affect others.

❺ Can a person obtain a happy attitude just by desiring to do so, or do circumstances simply bring happiness into one's life by chance? Explain your answer.

This question overlaps a bit with #4 above. As an individual, you decide whether to be happy or unhappy with whatever life gives you. Although everyone is affected by circumstances, people have more free choice than some believe. Once you start with the premise that happiness is a choice, the rest falls into place.

❻ What is meant by "flow"? Are there activities in your life in which you feel this optimal experience? Explain.

Flow is the term used by Csikszentmihalyi to describe the feeling you get when you are involved in activities that are completely absorbing, personally satisfying, and that fully engage your skills and talents. Activities that lead to flow (also described as an optimal experience) are challenging, goal-directed, and cause you to lose your self-awareness and perception of time.

Student answers will vary, but they should reflect the qualities just listed. Some students will list work-related activities, some will list school-related tasks, and some will list activities that revolve around family, hobbies, sports, or the outdoors.

❼ Thinking about your present workplace, does it seem to be managed more with Theory X or Theory Y beliefs? What workplace factors caused you to answer as you did? Do you feel you respond better to Theory X or Theory Y? Explain.

Theory X managers are described as believing that people hate to work; have to be forced, bribed, or threatened into working; don't want responsibility; and want job security above all else. Theory Y managers are described as believing that people see work as a natural activity, find rewards in doing their job well, like and seek responsibility, and are creative and original. They also believe that people's mental abilities are underused.

Student answers will vary as to whether their current workplace is managed more with Theory X or Theory Y principles, but should reflect the factors listed in the previous sentence.

Student responses will vary as to which type of manager they would respond better to, but most will say Theory Y.

8 **Looking at the suggestions in Strategy 4.2, think honestly of your everyday attitudes. Which of these suggestions could you improve upon, and in doing so build a more positive attitude?**

The suggestions in Strategy 4.2 include: be positive; don't get trapped in the negative attitudes of others; look for the good qualities in yourself, others, and your organization; don't let external situations push you around; and become goal-oriented.

Student responses will vary as to what they can do to build a more positive attitude.

Critical Thinking Questions

9 **Bad things do happen to everyone at one time or another. Is it always possible to maintain a positive attitude? Is it always necessary? Can you think of examples in which maintaining a positive attitude (at least temporarily) is impossible and unnecessary?**

Answers will vary, and there is no right or wrong answer. Students may list terrible tragedies (natural disasters, being a crime victim, death of a loved one, and so on) in which the most appropriate response would be grief or outrage. In such a situation, a positive attitude is not necessary and may not be possible, even temporarily, until the situation is resolved.

10 **In a recent study on stress and coping, researchers found that people facing a terrible problem (for example, taking care of a terminally ill family member) were better off if they could take a psychological "time out" by allowing themselves to enjoy ordinary events. These were simple events, such as admiring a beautiful sunset or pausing to think about a compliment they had received from someone else. They also took time to plan positive events, and to interpret neutral events in a positive way (for example, by looking for the humor in a situation). Can you think of a time when you have done this yourself? Do you think this would be a useful strategy for you? Could you try this positive "time out" the next time you face a long-term stressor, such as a difficult supervisor or coworker?**

Answers will vary. Some students will find this strategy useful, while others will not.

■ INTERNET EXERCISES

Tips for Teachers

1. **Self-Assessment** Ask students who have taken this test if they feel that optimism can be learned. Why or why not?

2. **Compare and Contrast** The Internet is full of surveys on job satisfaction. For polls of a different sort, refer students to *Dilbert.com* and suggest that they take some of its daily polls. The humorous tone will give students a good laugh, and you can ask them which poll was their favorite.

Working It Out

4.1 **Do You *Flow*?**

This exercise can be done in or out of class. In class seems to work better, but if assigned out of class, students will report their ideal "flow" activities in class. The activity students name should meet the eight descriptors for "flow" as identified in the text and in the instructions. This is a fun activity, but students can get carried away with some of their ideas.

Case Study

4.1 **Why Not "Y"?**

1. What type of management strategy does Susan seem to have that is affecting Rikki and Sergio in a negative way? What assumptions is Susan making about her employees?

Susan is using a Theory X management strategy with a group of employees who would be better off with a Theory Y manager.

Susan is assuming that her employees hate to work, have to be threatened or forced to work, don't want the responsibility of work, and just want job security. These employees seem to be creative people who like the satisfaction of working. They would probably respond better to a Theory Y manager.

2. Under what conditions, or for what types of employees, would Susan's management strategies perhaps be necessary?

If the employees at Metro were not very mature or responsible adults, they may respond better to a Theory X management strategy. If the work itself was boring, repetitive, dull, and even demeaning, a lack of employee satisfaction may require a Theory X manager in order to make them productive. If employees had been managed under Theory X for years and then Metro tried to institute a change to Theory Y overnight, employees may not respond. It does not sound as though any of these conditions are present at Metro.

3. If you were Rikki, what would you do to restore a positive attitude: confront Susan, say nothing to Susan and keep working at Metro, or look for a new job? What do you think the outcome of each of these choices would be?

Answers will vary. If Rikki confronts Susan, she may be fired (not an unlikely outcome with Theory X managers). If she keeps working there without saying anything, she will continue to be unhappy with her work environment because Susan will not be likely to change her management strategy. If she looks for a new job, she may find a better situation with a Theory Y manager or she may end up in the same boat.

The best possible outcome would be if she and other employees could approach Susan or Susan's boss in a way that is unthreatening to Susan's self-esteem, then talk about this situation. It is possible that Susan is basing her management strategy on incorrect assumptions and just needs to be told that employees are not as unwilling to work as she thinks they are. If she is committed to Theory X management, she may need direction from a higher-up to change her strategy.

4.2   Make Your Own Attitude

1. What is the basic problem at Candace's workplace?

The basic problem is just as Shelley stated: Candace is allowing the negative attitudes of others to pull her down. Negative attitudes can be contagious in a workplace.

2. Who really is responsible for Candace's attitudes: herself or her coworkers? What can she do to change to a more positive attitude?

Candace is ultimately responsible for her own attitudes. She can change them by trying the suggestions presented in this chapter: Be positive. Don't get trapped in others' negative attitudes. Look for the good in the situation. Don't get pushed around by outside situations. Become goal-oriented and work toward your goals. Candace could go through the steps outlined by Seligman after she defines the specific problem: Think of the worst thing that could happen, and what could prevent it; next, think of the best thing that could happen, and how to make that happen; and finally, think of the most likely thing that will happen, and how she will manage it if it happens.

Candace might also remember and work toward Myers' four characteristics of a happy person: healthy self-esteem, optimism, extraversion, and a sense of personal control.

3. If Candace continues to work at the same place without doing anything about her problem, what are some likely long-term outcomes?

The possible long-term outcomes of being unhappy at work include threats to self-esteem and physical health. She will likely find herself performing less well and becoming even less satisfied at work. Job performance and job satisfaction will continue to decline in a downward spiral. She will likely start missing work and face physical problems and illnesses. As she continues to be pulled into the negative attitudes of others, she will unwittingly erode the attitudes of still more people as well.

■ ADDITIONAL ACTIVITY

Check Your Attitude Toward Your Job

This activity can be done in class or out of class.

Purpose: This activity will allow you to think about the attitude you hold toward your job. After examining your score, think about things you can do to improve this attitude. Students who do not have outside employment can answer these questions in terms of their attitudes toward school.

Procedure: For each statement on page 24, pick the response that best describes your behavior at work in your present job and put that score next to the question. When you have finished, add up your score and compare it with the scoring guide below.

Attitude Toward My Job

Respond to the statements below in terms of your attitude at work or school, filling in the appropriate number next to the statement.

1=Never   2=Sometimes   3=Often   4=Almost Always   5=Always

_____ 1. When I daydream about what I would do if I won or inherited a large sum of money, I picture myself still working in this job.

_____ 2. I look forward to going to work every day.

_____ 3. My coworkers are happy to see me when I arrive at work.

_____ 4. I ignore rumors and gossip at work, and refuse to spread them.

_____ 5. I describe my job enthusiastically to people outside of work.

_____ 6. When people tell me about job openings elsewhere, I am uninterested and pretty much ignore them.

_____ 7. I am self-motivated and don't need to be prodded to get going at work.

_____ 8. I accept constructive criticism graciously and make the necessary changes.

_____ 9. My boss is pleased with the quality of my work.

_____ 10. I finish my work in a timely way, without procrastinating.

_____ 11. When extra work arises, I take care of it without complaining.

_____ 12. When something goes wrong at work or I make a mistake, I try to resolve the problem without blaming others or making excuses for myself.

_____ 13. I am friendly and polite with customers and coworkers.

_____ 14. If someone asks me to skip work or to go in late in order to do something more fun instead, I refuse.

_____ 15. I avoid making negative comments and complaining about my job.

_____ 16. Time goes by fast for me at work.

_____ 17. My coworkers tell me that I am doing good work, or that I seem to like my job.

_____ 18. I try to do my best with the tasks I do at work.

_____ 19. I am willing to work as a team member with my coworkers, rather than doing only what I would like to be doing on my own.

_____ 20. My coworkers and employers would say that, overall, I have a positive work attitude.

Negative attitude   **Positive attitude**
20 . . . . 30 . . . . 40 . . . . 50 . . . .60 . . . . 70 . . . . 80 . . . . 90 100

Looking at your score along this continuum, how positive is your attitude toward your job or school? Look at the areas you scored as "Sometimes" or "Never." What will you do to change these behaviors and improve your attitude?

Personal and Organizational Values

Chapter 5

LECTURE OUTLINE

I. Values Defined. Values are the worth or importance you attach to different factors in your life.
  A. Values exist within individuals and organizations. In organizations, a system of shared values is a **corporate culture**.
  B. Values are important in understanding human behavior because conflicts in the workplace are often based on differences in values.

II. Values Versus Attitudes. Your attitudes are often affected by your values. Values conflicts with other people certainly involve attitude problems; however, values are a deeper and more important part of everyone's lives and organizations.

III. Where Values Come From
  A. Personal values are formed in early childhood and are affected strongly by both the values of your parents and the values found in your environment. The historical period you grew up in also has a large effect on your values formation.
  B. How values have changed from past to present. Statistics expert Daniel Yankelovich shows that three new value patterns have emerged since the early 1970s:
    1. The nature of a person's paid job is now much more significant than it was.
    2. Leisure time is more valued now than before.
    3. Employees now insist strongly that jobs become less impersonal, more human and humane.
  C. Categories. (Refer students to Figure 5.1.) Values can be placed into two categories: **terminal values** and **instrumental values**.

IV. What Are Your Values? Answering this question requires a very high level of honesty.
  A. List at least ten activities or principles that are very important in your life, in any order.
  B. When you have listed the ten or more values, num-

ber them in their order of importance to you, then ask the person or people that are most important in your life to make a list of what that person *thinks* are your top ten values.
  C. Compare the two lists for differences and similarities.

V. Value Systems
  A. Eduard Spraunger has defined six different types of people, based on the types of value systems they have. **Spraunger's Six Value Systems** include:
    1. The theoretical person
    2. The economic person
    3. The aesthetic person
    4. The social person
    5. The political animal
    6. The religious human
  B. Graves' Seven Value Levels. Professor Clare Graves claims that people evolve through different levels of *psychological existence*. These levels describe changing values at different points in one's life:
    1. Level 1: React. This is called the reactive level of existence that is often associated with infancy: When a stimulus comes, it receives an expected response.
    2. Level 2: Tribalism. Tribalism includes dealing with fears of pain, discomfort, and lack of safety by giving in to the authority of a leader.
    3. Level 3: Egocentrism. Egocentrism is rugged individualism taken to an extreme. The egocentric is aggressive, restless, impulsive, and not inclined to follow the moral rules of society.
    4. Level 4: Conformity. Conformists are people who need clarity and straightforwardness. Vagueness frustrates them.
    5. Level 5: Achievement. These people try to reach success by manipulating people and situations to their own advantage.

6. Level 6: Socially Oriented. To the socially oriented, getting along is more important than getting ahead.

7. Level 7: Existentialism. These people do very well with vagueness, and get along well with people who don't share their own values. They usually have broad-based goals.

VI. **The Role of Integrity. Integrity** is often defined as soundness of moral character. Discuss the meaning of that definition with students, as well as another one: "Living up to the principles you claim to believe in."

   A. Reasons for the new emphasis on integrity in recent years.

   B. Stephen Covey's concept of **personality ethic** as opposed to the **character ethic**.

VII. **Values and the Workplace.** Values are the basis for both the purpose and the goals of an organization. Are your organization's values compatible with your personal values?

VIII. **Values Conflicts.** These can take several forms. All of these are important to a study of human relations.

   A. Interpersonal values conflicts are conflicts with others that focus on values differences.

   B. Personal versus group values conflicts are between the values of the individual and those of the group.

   C. Internal Values Conflicts. Especially important to this issue is the **cognitive dissonance** theory, which teaches that you can rectify cognitive dissonance by (choose any one of the following):
      1. changing your original beliefs.
      2. using **denial**.
      3. using **self-justification**.
      4. changing your behavior.

IX. **Values in an International Economy.** The U.S. is now dealing with people from many different religions, political systems, cultural backgrounds, and ethnic groups. Everyone needs to understand that each country has the same temptation to think its own national and culture values are the best. Four major areas of international values differences are:

   A. differing views of power and authority.
   B. differing views of the value of individuals and groups.
   C. tolerance for uncertainty.
   D. the value of punctuality.

 5.1 Redefining Your Personal Values: The Rath Test. Student answers will vary.

1. Did I choose this value freely, with no outside pressure?
2. Did I choose this value from several alternatives?
3. Did I consider the consequences of my choice?
4. Do I like and respect this value?
5. Will I defend this value publicly?
6. Will I base my behavior on this value?
7. Do I find this value persistent throughout my life?

 5.2 Building a Character Ethic for Integrity

1. Focus: Ask yourself what you really want from life.
2. Respect: Do you respect yourself and demand respect from others?
3. Responsibility: Accept full responsibility for your own life.
4. Pride: Practice feeling good about yourself. (Revisit Chapter 2 on self-esteem if you find it appropriate.)
5. Fairness and Equity: Believe in and defend the rights of others.
6. Trust and Being Trusted: Trust others and develop others' trust in yourself.

ANSWERS TO IN-CHAPTER QUESTIONS

PHOTO, page 125: What risks do you think Janet took when she approached her supervisor with her problem?

Janet took the risk that she could be demoted to a less demanding, lower paying position. She also could have been asked to leave the company if there were no suitable positions available.

PHOTO, page 127: Do you feel that your needs are better met by online shopping than by traditional methods?

This depends on what you are buying, as well as your comfort level with making purchases over the Internet. Everyday purchases such as food are probably easier to buy through traditional methods, but perhaps you prefer using the Internet for finding hard-to-find items like used books or antiques.

FIGURE 5.1, page 129: How do you see these differences in other generations?

This depends on your generation, your personal experience, and also on your generation's typical views of other age groups. For instance, many baby boomers reject certain aspects of their parents' generation, but many Generation X'ers like much of what happened in the 1960s.

FIGURE 5.2, page 130: Can you think of an instrumental value of yours that is helping you achieve a terminal value?

Examples will vary, but one instrumental value can be "Working hard to get promoted," and the terminal value could be "So that my spouse and I can have a comfortable life and retirement."

PHOTO, page 133: Which of Graves' seven levels best fits your personality?

Your answer will depend on your maturity level, but you may also find that you are in a combination of two or more levels, depending on your mood and the situation.

PHOTO, page 136: How have you handled interpersonal values conflicts in the past?

There are countless ways to handle this type of conflict. You may have handled them by discussing your differences, by ignoring them, or by transferring to another department or leaving the company.

PHOTO, page 141: What is your tolerance for uncertainty?

This depends not only on cultural factors, but on other factors, such as your fear level, your enjoyment of risk, and the importance of the issue at hand.

PHOTO, page 144: Are your values really ones that you consider your own and would defend publicly?

Your answer will depend on how you developed these values. If you adopted them from other people, or from some kind of peer pressure, without really integrating them into your beliefs in a meaningful way, then they are probably not your own values. If, however, these values truly match your core beliefs, they are likely your own.

CHAPTER REVIEW, pages 147–152

Review Questions

❶ How do values develop during the early part of people's lives?

In early childhood your values are affected strongly by the values of your parents and by other forces and people in your environment. Values formation is also affected by the era, geographical location, and strength of family bonds. As people grow older, peer group members become increasingly influential in the formation of values.

❷ What is the difference between terminal and instrumental values? Give examples of each.

Terminal values are values that are likely to persist throughout life. ("Until we terminate," if students need a memory peg.) Instrumental values are based on actions and attitudes, and will often be closely linked to one or more terminal values.

Figure 5.2 is an extensive list of possible examples of both terminal and instrumental values. Students will likely think of other examples.

❸ How have values changed over the past several decades? Are the values of today's society the same as your personal values? If not, how do they differ?

The first part of this question is quite objective and fact-based; the rest is subjective. During the past several decades, values have changed dramatically. Daniel Yankelovich mentions three changes:

1. The nature of a person's paid job is now much more significant than it once was. A few years ago, the amount of money one made overrode the

nature of the job more than it now does—both in terms of status and job satisfaction.

2. Leisure time is more valuable than it used to be. 20 years ago, popular magazines predicted moral decay because of excessive free time caused by more and more leisure time. In fact, the exact opposite has happened. Many people in America have more money than time to spare. Hence, the popularity of small businesses that return library books and rented videotapes, answer phone calls, and pay monthly bills for people who are too busy to take care of such details in their lives.

3. Not only must jobs be more meaningful, but employees are insisting that the workplace become more human and humane.

Students might also mention the impact of the 1960s on the baby boomers and the frustration felt by today's college graduates (sometimes called the baby busters). Another change has to do with the high divorce rate and the change on family emphasis. Another good discussion topic is whether the 21st century is leaning to a return to the nuclear family.

One method of approaching this question is to refer students to Figure 5.1 and lead the class through a discussion of all of the items listed. If you as the instructor keep the discussion moving, it can be interesting and meaningful to students.

4 **How can you be sure that the values that you think you have are really your own?**

The Rath Test in Strategy 5.1 is the basis for an intelligent answer to this question. Students should ask themselves:

1. Did I choose this value freely, with no outside pressure?
2. Did I choose this value from several alternatives?
3. Did I consider the consequences of my choice?
4. Do I like and respect this value?
5. Will I defend this value publicly?
6. Will I base my behavior on this value?
7. Do I find this value persistent through my life?

You could explore each of these questions in class, discussing why each question is important and what types of nonvalues each one might reveal.

Beyond that approach, students should be encouraged to use this test on their top five stated values, as suggested in the text. Since the material is quite personal, in most classes it will likely be best left to personal homework.

5 **What is the *personality ethic* as opposed to the *character ethic*? Which one affects your behavior more? Explain.**

The **personality ethic** is manipulative and self-serving, and those who employ it see success as a function of personality, public image, behaviors, skills and techniques. The **character ethic**, on the other hand, stresses integrity, humility, fidelity, courage, justice, patience, and the Golden Rule. For a complete understanding of Covey and a discussion of these topics, see Stephen R. Covey, *The Seven Habits of Highly Successful People* (New York: Simon & Schuster, 1990), pp. 18–21.

6 **What is a values conflict? Have you ever been involved in a conflict that involved values differences? If so, what was the focus of the conflict? Interpersonal? You (or someone else) against the group? Internal?**

Of course, only the first part of this question can be answered here. The second half will get responses responded to with a variety of emphasis points. The three ways in which values conflict can manifest itself are:

1. Interpersonal values conflict. When two or more people with differing values are attempting to relate to one another, values conflict can take place between them. This type of conflict can be negative or positive, depending on the way the individuals deal with the issues.
2. Personal versus group values. This type of values conflict often involves a clash between an individual's personal values and those established by the group to which he or she belongs or is attempting to belong. For example, sometimes an individual will begin a job where workgroups hold collective values that challenge or threaten him or her. Case #1 (Group Values at the Car Wash) illustrates this type of values conflict.
3. Internal values conflict. This values conflict is waged within the individual. To explain this type of conflict fully, the student should use and define the term **cognitive dissonance**, which can be defined as desiring two different outcomes that contradict each other.

7 **Define *integrity*. What steps can you take to make integrity a part of your own personal value system?**

The textbook defines **integrity** as soundness of moral character. Other people have defined it as living up to the principles that one claims to believe in.

The second part of the question can be both complex and interesting and is a great discussion question for a certain type of student group. The first step toward making integrity a part of one's own personal value system would be to make a series of decisions as to what is important in your life and in others' lives as you must relate to them. From there, one must construct a set of convictions about the important values and how to enact them in daily life.

8 **What is cognitive dissonance? How is an understanding of cognitive dissonance important to your understanding of your own values and how you act—or fail to act—on them?**

Cognitive dissonance is the feeling of discomfort that people experience when they perform an action that is not consistent with their customary conceptions of themselves; it is a key source of internal conflict. The most intense manifestation of cognitive dissonance is when people act in a way that threatens or disrupts the positive image they have of themselves.

Students need to understand that cognitive dissonance forces individuals to confront the discrepancy between who they think they are and how they actually behave.

Good class illustrations are people who smoke cigarettes daily although they know that doing so is a serious health risk. Such people will either:

1. find support for a belief that smoking isn't damaging to health. For example, George Burn's smoked 12 cigars a day and lived to be 100, and Winston Churchill smoked heavily and lived into his 90s.
2. deny to themselves and others that they smoke even a fraction of what they actually smoke.
3. add new beliefs to reduce the contradiction and justify themselves. For example, "Yes, cigarette smoking is harmful, but that's only American cigarettes. If I smoke a European brand, the health risks will be so low it won't matter." Or, "The carbon filters reduce the harmful effects to nearly zero."
4. change their behavior by stopping smoking.

Critical Thinking Questions

9 **How culturally determined are the values that you hold dear? What are the differences in how the four factors of values deal with other cultures?**

The first part of the question is subjective and will be answered individually by each student. The student who has read and thought about it will likely be aware that values are very likely to be at least somewhat culturally determined. Students who have lived in different cultures will be very aware of this issue and can be called upon for useful feedback when these questions are discussed in class.

The four factors of values differences are:

1. Views of power and authority. In many emerging countries, the prevailing attitude toward management is that what a manager says must be followed without question.

2. Views of the individual versus the group. In many countries, the group is seen as considerably more important than any of its individual members.
3. Tolerance for uncertainty. To many cultures, maximizing certainty is a high value; to others, such as the U.S., it is not. Those that work with other cultures must keep in mind that they may not share the same value.
4. The value of punctuality. In the U.S. people are often judged by how punctual they are. In many other cultures, time-urgency is not a value at all.

These four areas of difference can help you in understanding the values misunderstandings that Americans might have with members of other cultures. To be sure, many other values differences exist besides those mentioned here. Remember to be aware that some of your values are considered less important by other groups—and vice versa.

10 **Have you ever experienced cognitive dissonance in your own life? (More than likely, you have experienced it more than once.) How did you react? What strategies did you use to lessen the impact of the dissonance in your life?**

The dissonance invariably causes an uncomfortable feeling. Once people have this feeling, they will do one of a number of things to reduce the discomfort level. They will usually act in one of four ways to reduce cognitive dissonance:

1. They will try to justify their behavior by changing one of the cognitions—usually either the behavior or the belief or value. Changing one's original beliefs would be an example.
2. They will use denial to remove the dissonance.
3. They will try to add new beliefs or behaviors that will make sense out of the contradiction, using self-justification.
4. They will change their behavior to make it conform to the dissonant cognition.

Cognitive dissonance must be examined carefully, especially in terms of honesty to oneself. If you are to understand your values consistently, you must be aware of the very human tendency to use the less honest forms of reasoning that lead to cognitive dissonance.

Tips for Teachers

1. **Research and Write** Ask students about what their previous understanding of civic values was before visiting this Web site; although many students may have heard this term before, they may not fully know what it means. How did this site enhance their knowledge of civic values?

2. **Self-Assessment** Ask students why they chose the various communication attributes that they did; what did those attributes mean to them? Did they agree with the site's evaluation?

Working It Out

5.1 Values and Your Career Choice

This is best used as a take-home exercise to enhance the application of course material to the student's daily life and decision making. Either before or after students have completed the questionnaire, a brief class discussion can enhance the exercise's value.

Case Study

5.1 Group Values at the Car Wash

1. Describe the values of Tony Henneberg and contrast them with the group values at the car wash.

Tony seems to value learning and knowledge much more than his coworkers do. He also values going to bars and nightclubs less than they do. He respects professors more and isn't ashamed of getting high grades. His ultimate life goal—and his terminal values—are also much different than theirs. One could argue, though, that Tony simply chose to conform to another set of norms.

2. Besides quitting, could Tony have done anything to correct the obvious human relations problems caused by the difference in values?

Since the dean's list was public knowledge, no amount of skillful acting would have convinced Tony's coworkers that he was one of them. He could have started going to bars and telling his coworkers about it, which

may have elicited some respect. However, the attitude toward barhopping was at least as important as doing it.

3. Suppose Tony had not received the scholarship. Could he have survived at the car wash until the end of his senior year? If so, how?

Tony could simply decide that his acceptance by coworkers wasn't important. He could perform his job as effectively as possible and cope with the rest. This approach would require a high tolerance for rejection—and stress. He could also fake his values and pretend to care about the bar scene, but this would not have changed his coworkers' knowledge of the dean's list. With no one accepting him, his status with the owner could even become muddied, especially if a coworker were to sabotage Tony's work.

Case Study

5.2 Honest Jane

1. It seems clear at this point that Jane is not a thief. However, based on her values, what would you expect her to do at this point?

Students will, of course, have differing opinions on what Jane should do. Their answers to this question will also have a direct bearing on their answers to question #3. The best thing to do here is to list the possible actions Jane could take, along with the probable consequences of each choice.

2. Do you think that Jane's value of "not being self-righteous" will keep her from telling management what she has seen?

Students can use this question to examine the issue of cognitive dissonance. The issue is made more complex by the collision of values that Jane might be encountering. For example, if she should use choice #3 in the above question, won't the uneasy feeling of letting Louis get away with blatant theft produce cognitive dissonance—as would #2, to an even greater extent? Yet, if Jane were to tell on Lou, cognitive dissonance could be the result based on her value that says a person should not be self-righteous.

3. Based on your own values, what would you do if you were Jane? Why?

The question is obviously quite subjective, and student answers will vary widely.

Chapter 6

Motivation: Increasing Productivity

LECTURE OUTLINE

I. What Is Motivation? Motivation is the willingness to make an effort toward accomplishment.
  A. Organizational climate is the emotional "weather" in a workplace. It can be warm, which encourages motivation and morale; or cold, which discourages motivation.
  B. Morale is the overall mood of a group of people, based on employee satisfaction. High morale encourages motivation.
II. General Theories of Motivation
  A. McGregor's Theories X and Y. See Chapter 4 for an introduction to Theories X and Y.
    1. Theory X managers see employees as needing to be forced to work.
    2. Theory Y managers see employees as enjoying work.
  B. Extrinsic Rewards. Theory X sees employees as motivated more by extrinsic, or external, factors. These include performance bonuses, profit sharing programs, impressive titles, pay raises, and preferred offices, office furnishings, and lunch hours.
  C. Intrinsic Rewards. Theory Y sees employees as motivated more by intrinsic, or internal, rewards, such as satisfaction, self-identity, self-fulfillment, self-worth, a work ethic, the social value of the work, fulfilling social and community roles, personal growth, responsibility, variety of activities, job freedom, interesting tasks, and the opportunity to make decisions.
III. Need-Based Theories of Motivation
  A. Maslow's hierarchy of needs states that people are motivated by their needs, which are fulfilled in a specific order: **physiological, safety/security, love/belongingness, esteem,** and **self-actualization.**
  B. According to McClelland's **manifest needs theory,** people are motivated by individual needs for **power, affiliation** (the need to be with others), and **achievement.**

IV. Behavior-Based Theories of Motivation. In Vroom's **expectancy theory,** people are motivated by expecting valued rewards to result from increased effort (**expectancy**).
  A. Instrumentality is the likelihood that something good (or bad) will result from the increase in effort and performance.
  B. Valence is the value a person places on that reward.
V. Reinforcement Theory and Behavior Modification. Skinner's **behavior modification theory** (also called **reinforcement**) states that when people associate a behavior with a reward that they desire, they will be motivated to increase the behavior in order to get the reward.
  A. Reinforcers or incentives come from external sources just as extrinsic rewards do, but instead address internal or intrinsic motivation.
  B. Reinforcers are more effective when employees have the opportunity for **goal setting.**
VI. Motivation and Self-Esteem
  A. Low self-esteem can motivate a person not to work.
  B. High self-esteem can motivate a person to succeed.

6.1 Applying McClelland's Theory
1. Ask your students what they would do upon becoming a billionaire. This can give clues to a person's needs for power, affiliation, or achievement.
2. Does your job meet your needs profile?
3. Managers should look at how the work their employees are doing meets their needs.

6.2 Changing Your Behavior
1. Skinner's idea of **shaping** can be used to change a behavior in yourself that you want to change.
2. In shaping a behavior, you identify a specific goal behavior to change, or identify small steps that will lead to the change, and reward yourself.

ANSWERS TO IN-CHAPTER QUESTIONS

PHOTO, page 155: Why did Liza lose motivation so quickly? Did the things that motivated her have anything to do with her quick disappointment in her job?

The long work hours and difficult supervisor proved to be greater stressors than Liza had anticipated. The increase in pay that initially motivated her was not enough to satisfy her other needs.

FIGURE 6.1, page 157: Which theory seems most accurate to you?

Your answer will depend on your perception of yourself and your needs. For instance, if you see yourself as progressing through life with gradually higher goals, perhaps Maslow's theory is best for you. On the other hand, if you see yourself as made up of basic interconnecting elements, such as the needs to have power and achieve things, McClelland's theory may sound better.

FIGURE 6.2, page 160: Which rewards do you feel are more valuable?

Many people would say intrinsic rewards because they feel that enjoying their jobs is most important. However, high pay and exciting job perks can make a mundane job not just bearable, but rewarding; in cases like this, extrinsic rewards can be more valuable.

FIGURE 6.3, page 161: At which level do you see yourself right now? Do you see yourself in more than one level at once?

Your current level depends on which of your needs are fulfilled and which you are seeking to fulfill.

FIGURE 6.4, page 163: What is holding you back in your self-actualization?

Often, people are held back by fears of losing security, lack of self-esteem, or simply the fact that they've never examined their true needs.

PHOTO, page 169: How can positive reinforcement help motivate employees?

Positive reinforcement by compliments (also called stroking) can help employees' esteem needs, as well as strengthen their feelings of affiliation and achievement.

CHAPTER REVIEW, pages 175–179

Review Questions

❶ Which of the motivation theories that you've just learned about best explains why Liza Valenti's experience in the opening story ends the way it does? Why?

Answers will vary.

According to Theory X and Theory Y, the management strategy that Liza's supervisor was using did not fit with Liza's work motivations. Her boss sounds like a Theory X employee, and Liza sounds like an employee who would be happier with Theory Y management.

According to the needs-based theories, Maslow might have said that Liza had a need for esteem or belongingness that wasn't being met as evidenced by a boss who didn't make her feel good about her work, and her feeling that she didn't have enough "belongingness" time with her children. The high salary would have allowed her to meet her physiological and safety needs,

so she would have moved up from those levels. McClelland would have said that her needs for affiliation and achievement aren't being met.

The behavior-based theories would say that this job isn't rewarding to her. Skinner would say that it does not provide positive reinforcement that motivates her. Her boss sounds as though he does not provide much reinforcement in the form of encouraging feedback. It sounds as though Liza feels there are no intrinsic rewards in this job, even though she initially was happy with the extrinsic reward of high pay. Vroom would say that the value, or valence, of the pay is no longer rewarding enough for Liza.

❷ What can employees and managers do to improve an organizational climate?

Answers will vary, but employees can take a look at the situation where the organizational climate feels cold and see what they can do to improve it for themselves. Incorporating information from earlier chapters, one can see that they may be absorbing the negative attitudes of others. If so, they may only need to improve their attitudes at work or refuse to take on the negative attitudes of others.

For their part, managers should start with their own attitudes in trying to improve the organizational climate at work. They can look at the physical environment and see if it is stifling or depressing, at the level of harmony between employees and their job assignments to see if improvements can be made, and at procedures to see if these can be streamlined or made to include employees in decision-making in order to improve the organizational climate for everyone. Managers should also be good enough watchers and listeners to notice discontented employees.

In addition to the factors just listed, managers should watch for personality clashes and other non-task-related sources of disharmony. These sources could include noise level, organizational architecture, and open or closed communication systems. Before making changes to improve the organizational climate, the manager should discuss the changes with employees.

This question can be expanded in class by asking students to describe past jobs where the climate was really negative, then getting them to explain the factors that made it so negative. Other students might be interested in discussing jobs they have had with really positive organizational climates, and explaining why these climates were more effective. For the bolder instructor, classroom climate is another related topic.

❸ What is a needs theory? Considering Maslow's hierarchy of needs, do you see yourself on this hierarchy? Where? What do you need in order to become self-actualized?

A needs theory is based on the assumption that people are motivated to satisfy or fulfill a need for something. When those needs can be tied to the workplace, the manager and employee both have a point of reference for understanding the needs of the employee in relation to both the job and the workplace.

Answers regarding Maslow's hierarchy will vary. Students who talk about extreme poverty and trying to make certain they have enough to eat on a daily basis are describing themselves as being on the lowest level, physiological needs. Students who say they are sleeping on a friend's couch or trying to find a place (or even a safer

place) to live are on the second level, safety needs. Students who say they are joining clubs on campus, trying to meet people at work, or looking for someone to date are on the third level, belongingness and love. Students who describe themselves as trying to excel at work or school are on the fourth level, esteem needs. Some students may describe themselves as being motivated by learning new things, so they would be on the cognitive needs level. Some students may say they are motivated to find beauty or to discover wonderful works of literature, which suggests the aesthetic needs level. Remember that these two levels, cognitive and aesthetic needs, are not technically in this model. As motivators, they lie between the fourth need, esteem, and the fifth need, self-actualization.

Few students will accurately describe themselves as being the best they can be, not needing others, and having accomplished everything they wanted to in life; but if they say this, they are describing themselves as being on the self-actualization level, the highest level in the model. It is more likely that students will say that those are the things they are working toward as they begin to fulfill their self-actualization needs.

Students who find fault with Maslow's theory should be made aware that he was the pioneer in motivational psychology. Before him, no one had attempted to formalize an explanation of why people work. Although the Hawthorne Studies provided a breakthrough in motivation research when Elton Mayo saw employees' ego needs as a major factor in motivation, that single factor does not constitute a formalized theory. In addition, Maslow himself knew that his hierarchy doesn't answer every question about human motivation.

❹ Which of the three needs in McClelland's manifest needs theory (power, affiliation, or achievement), motivates you the most?

Answers will vary. Responses that suggest a need for controlling others and taking power will suggest a need for power. Responses that suggest a need to be with others, and to be accepted and liked, will suggest a higher need for affiliation. Responses that suggest working toward goals, taking on activities that require a high energy level, or taking personal responsibility for some accomplishment suggest a higher need for achievement. McClelland also suggested that these needs could be exercised and developed like a muscle, or changed with effort.

❺ How do the two needs theories developed by Maslow and McClelland differ from each other? How are they similar?

In Maslow's theory, the needs occur in a specific order for everyone. Needs that aren't yet satisfied will motivate behavior to satisfy them, and once a need has been met, it is no longer motivating. In McClelland's theory, needs are separate and distinct from each other. In contrast to Maslow, McClelland says everyone has different combinations of concurrent needs for power, achievement, and affiliation. McClelland's needs are not hierarchical, so people don't go through each in turn; they just have differing amounts.

Maslow and McClelland both see people as being motivated to satisfy particular needs. In this way, they are similar.

6 **Which motivates you more, intrinsic rewards or extrinsic rewards? When you imagine getting an "A" in your human relations class, are you more motivated by the tangible rewards of a higher GPA or the self-satisfaction of a job well done?**

Answers will vary.

7 **Why does positive reinforcement seem to work? Can you think of examples in your life where positive reinforcement was used successfully? Unsuccessfully?**

Answers will vary. Students will probably respond that they like to work for rewards rather than for punishments. Threats of punishment are threats to self-esteem, and people respond better to a reward that builds self-esteem rather than one that hurts it.

Examples of successful application of positive reinforcement will vary.

Students may include examples such as working at school for extra credit, or working on the job for bonuses or praise. Examples from elementary school often arise here, with descriptions of token economies in which students earn points toward a reward. As an example, a third-grader is tardy after recess nearly every day, causing disruption to her classroom. One school counselor gives her a small card on which there are ten spaces for rubber stamps. The stamp is the picture of a dog or cat. When ten animal stamps have been placed on the card, one for each day the student was on time, the student has earned a reward such as ice cream at lunch. The reward is chosen on the basis of the child's desires (whatever self-selected reward will motivate the child). The next step is that the child starts another animal stamp card, but this time the ten days must be consecutive. This process continues until the behavior has been satisfactorily modified.

Examples of unsuccessful application of positive reinforcement will vary.

Students may offer examples that illustrate resentment at having been manipulated by others, perhaps attempts to motivate them to work for a reinforcer that they did not want or one that was not powerful enough to motivate them. Also, it is often the case that positive reinforcement does not work because of an error in

implementation of the plan. Ask questions about the details of the process.

8 **Overall, which motivation theory do *you* like best? Why?**

Answers will vary. Responses based on needs-based theories should mention Maslow's hierarchy of needs (physiological, safety, belongingness, esteem, self-actualization; perhaps cognitive or aesthetic needs) or McClelland's needs model (need for power, affiliation, or achievement).

Responses addressing behavior-based models should mention Vroom's expectancy theory and its components (expectancy, instrumentality, valence) or Skinner's behavior-based motivation (positive reinforcement) or behavior modification. Some students will discuss intrinsic or extrinsic rewards (internal or external), or Theories X and Y (employees need prodding, or employees enjoy working).

One caution from experience: Students often express their "favorite" theory (especially in a written exercise on this question), when they are actually explaining the only one of the theories they understand enough to explain.

Instructors may want to also ask students to explain what they dislike about all the other theories.

Critical Thinking Questions

9 **Some people believe that trying to find a way to motivate others is somewhat unethical or manipulative. What are your views? Has there been a time when you have felt this was happening to you?**

Answers will vary. In American culture, manipulation is considered by most as offensive since it threatens one's individuality. Students should recognize, however, that attempts at motivating or manipulating others occur virtually constantly. These include persuasive attempts by advertisers, instructors, parents, employers, peers, religious institutions, and society in general.

10 **The intrinsic rewards of a job can be very motivating. Some people think that intrinsic motivation is nobler than behavior motivated by extrinsic rewards such as money. Is intrinsic motivation a nobler type of motivation than external rewards?**

Answers will vary. This question can present an interesting philosophical debate among students. Some will say that any reward is still a reward, whether intrinsic or extrinsic; neither is more noble than the other. Other students will say that working for an external reward plays into unnecessary materialistic greed and is therefore less noble or moral than being motivated by intrinsic rewards.

INTERNET EXERCISES

Tips for Teachers

1. **Compare and Contrast** Ask students if this exercise made them aware of how motivating (or unmotivating) their current job really is. Did they gain any knowledge of what they could do to make an unmotivating job less so?

2. **Self-Assessment** Ask students who have taken the Kingdomality quiz if any of them have read a book that covers similar concepts, *What Color is Your Parachute?* If they have, ask them to compare the approaches and evaluations of the two resources. If not, ask them if they think that the Kingdomality test covered enough ground to render an accurate evaluation.

Working It Out

6.1 What Career Motivates You?

This exercise is self-explanatory. In most cases, it doesn't work except as an out of class assignment. After the out of class work has been done, though, an in class evaluative component can be used. Students can meet in groups of two and evaluate the findings of the interviews, comparing and contrasting their experiences.

Case Study

6.1 What Do Kids Need?

1. Is Maria right? Does it seem that Stacy, Ayako, Jorge, Mike, and Jamal are on different levels of Maslow's hierarchy of needs? On what level would you place each of them ?

Maslow's needs hierarchy would work in this situation to explain the needs each child is expressing. Stacy seems motivated by physiological needs (hunger), and Ayako by security (emotional, as evidenced by clinging to Maria's hand during the entire recess). Jorge and Mike seem to be motivated by their need to belong (as they try to join the soccer game with the other kids), and Jamal by esteem needs (he is trying to gain Maria's approval and verification of his baseball skills).

2. How can Maria use this theory to motivate the children in their school work?

Once she has identified each child's level in the hierarchy, Maria can address their needs during class time. She can give Stacy little food rewards, reward Ayako with extra attention or time so that she feels secure, reward Jorge and Mike with helping them learn skills that will enable them to be accepted by other children, and reward Jamal with extra boosts to his self-esteem.

3. Compare Maslow's needs model with McClelland's. Which of McClelland's needs seems to be important for each child?

McClelland's theory is not so straightforward to apply here. None of the children seem to be trying to control others or exert power, except to gain affiliation or achievement recognition. Stacy does not seem motivated by any of the needs McClelland identifies. Ayako, Jorge, and Mike all seem motivated by affiliation needs, and Jamal by achievement needs.

Case Study

6.2 Holidays at Olson's

1. How can you explain the strange reaction of the cabinet shop employees to this well-meant holiday present from a thankful boss?

The jackets were not seen as a motivator by these employees. In Skinner's words, they were an ineffective positive reinforcer. In Vroom's words, the jackets lacked valence for these employees. Maslow and McClelland would say the jackets did not satisfy a need. The employees would have been happier with a different extrinsic motivator: raises.

2. What steps should Randy Olson have taken before making the decision to order the jackets?

Randy should have checked with his employees for ideas about what they would like as a thank-you. They might have responded better to bonuses, paid time off, improvements to the break room, a dinner in their honor with certificates of appreciation, or other intrinsic or extrinsic motivators. If he wanted to surprise them with a gift without leaking the plan, he could have had floor supervisors scout for ideas. Whatever method he used to get information about what they would have liked better, it should have involved finding out more about their needs and desires.

3. What facts and theories about motivation could have prevented this expensive incident? Would McClelland's needs theory have helped?

Maslow's theory would at least have alerted him to the concept of needs levels. What needs level are his employees on? Maybe they need cash bonuses because many of them are still on one of the lower levels of the hierarchy. McClelland's theory would have made Olson sensitive to the needs profiles of his various employees. If affiliation needs are not being met, a recreation break room might have been the answer. The jackets that identified them as part of the Olson family were not effective. One possibility is that the needs for power and achievement were being underemphasized by the work situation, and the jackets certainly did not help.

Olson assumed they would respond best to an extrinsic reward, but this may be incorrect. Skinner's theory would suggest Olson find out what reward these employees would respond to, and then provide that. Vroom would say the jackets did not have motivational value.

■ ADDITIONAL ACTIVITY

What Motivates You?

This gives students another way of examining their own motivation, comparing and contrasting their motivational profiles with those of other students.

Important note to instructor: This exercise should be undertaken at the very beginning of the unit on motivation, preferably *before* students have read Chapter 6.

Begin this exercise with students working individually. Have them rank the ten qualities below, using the Individual Rankings column. The easiest way to rank these is to start with the top three, then go to the bottom three; then fill in the four in the middle. Students can then compare their answers with those of other people, or rank these in importance in a small group by consensus.

This exercise allows you to integrate your explanation of McClelland's theory into a survey allowing students to develop their motivation profile in terms of McClelland's three needs areas: achievement, power, and affiliation. If most of the items they rated high have fallen predominantly into one of these three areas, they can make some tentative generalizations about their own motivation before going on to further study in the chapter.

Key for Evaluation Using McClelland's Needs Theory

1. Wages and salary . . . . .Achievement Needs
2. Good relationships with coworkers . . . . .Affiliation Needs
3. Challenge level of the job or tasks . . . . .Achievement Needs
4. Likelihood of being promoted . . . . .Power Needs
5. Security of the job . . . . .Achievement Needs
6. Amount of independence allowed on the job . . . . . . .Power Needs
7. Status of the job . . . . .Power Needs
8. Quality of supervision . . . . .Affiliation Needs
9. Recognition given . . . . .Power and Achievement Needs
10. Feeling of achievement . . . . .Achievement Needs

Job Qualities	Individual Rankings	Group Rankings
1. Wages and salary	_____	_____
2. Good relationships with coworkers	_____	_____
3. Challenge level of the job or tasks	_____	_____
4. Likelihood of being promoted	_____	_____
5. Security of the job	_____	_____
6. Amount of independence allowed on the job	_____	_____
7. Status of the job	_____	_____
8. Quality of supervision	_____	_____
9. Recognition given	_____	_____
10. Feeling of achievement	_____	_____

Communication and Human Relations

LECTURE OUTLINE

I. **Communication and Miscommunication. Communication** is the giving and receiving of ideas, feelings, and information among people; it can be verbal and non-verbal, through speaking or listening.
   A. Without effective communication, no workplace can function properly; miscommunication wastes billions of dollars a year in American industry alone.
   B. False assumptions lie at the heart of many miscommunication. It also wastes time and damages human relations.

II. **Listening—and How It Can Fail**
   A. People have a very strong need to have other people hear them, understand them, and process the information they give.
      1. This tremendous need to be listened to is crucial to human relations.
      2. When listening is purposely withheld, one's self-esteem suffers.
   B. Selective listening. American society is bombarded with messages. Because people could not possibly give their full attention to all of these messages, they engage in **selective listening**.
      1. **Information overload** is one cause of poor listening skills.
      2. When a subject seems too difficult, people will often fail to listen.
      3. The opposite often happens as well: For example, when people are listening to a single speaker, they can easily allow their minds to wander.
   C. Tuning out. Sometimes, people in the workplace simply refuse to listen to coworkers, often out of **prejudice**.
      1. **Red flag words** and expressions can bring an immediate emotional response from the listener.
      2. There are many other reasons why people do not hear what their coworkers are really saying, but **active listening** helps people get beyond those reasons.

III. **The Timing of Messages.** Timing can determine whether a message becomes distorted and misunderstood.
   A. Emotional timing refers to the emotional readiness someone has to hear a message.
   B. Situational timing refers to the listener's situation when a message is received. Privacy is usually the key element.
   C. Relevance timing is similar to situational timing, and simply means that communication should fit the other topic being discussed at a given time.
   D. **Filtering** is when listeners fail to receive messages correctly because of "hearing what they want to hear."

IV. **Communicating Without Words.** Another area related to listening skills is *nonverbal communication*. **Nonverbals** are what you express through actions rather than words. (Refer students to Figure 7.2.)

V. **Functions of Nonverbal Messages**
   A. They show the feelings and emotions of the speaker.
   B. They help clarify what is being said in words.
      1. Nonverbal communication allows you to understand and interpret what is meant in terms of the context in which it is being said.
      2. **Context** is a point of reference—a place from which to begin.
   C. They show the **intensity** and emotional reactions of the speaker to the listener, whether those reactions are negative, positive, or mixed.
   D. By observing someone's gestures, you can tell a great deal about how open or closed the other person is in his or her attitude. Every gesture you use falls into one of these four categories:
      1. **Illustrators** are gestures used to clarify a point you are making. An example would be pointing the way down the street when giving directions, or pounding a fist on the podium to emphasize a point when speaking in public.

2. **Regulators** are used to control the flow of communication. When you raise your hand in class to get attention, you are using a regulator.

3. **Displays** are gestures you use as nonverbal punctuation marks. An example would be the "cut off" sign to signal a public speaker that his or her time is up.

4. **Emblems** are gestures used in a specific manner because they have a specific meaning, usually one understood by both sender and receiver. During World War II, Winston Churchill was known for his "V for victory" gesture, which all of the allied nations understood and appreciated.

E. **Distancing** (also called *proxemics*) is the distance between speakers.

1. Everyone carries around a bubble of space.

2. In some cultures, being very close to another person is much more acceptable than in America or in most European cultures.

3. As the world becomes more and more an international community, learning the norms of other societies will become increasingly important.

VI. **Communicating in an Organization**

A. **Organizational communication** has formal and informal dimensions.

1. When it follows the organizational chart upward and downward, it is called **vertical communication.**

2. **Horizontal communication** refers to messages between you and other people who are equal to you in the formal organization. Even in horizontal communication, care needs to be taken to communicate without causing problems for yourself and others in the company.

B. Grapevines

1. Every company contains an informal organization, made up of relationships that establish themselves naturally.

2. It tends to communicate through an incomplete but mostly accurate network known as the **grapevine.**

3. The grapevine is usually called the **rumor mill** when it contains mostly false information.

4. When companies have poor formal lines of communication, the grapevine becomes even more important.

VII. **International and Intercultural Organizations.** The average American is ill-equipped to communicate with people from other cultures.

A. Edward T. Hall has identified different cultures as being **low-context cultures** and **high-context cultures**.

1. In low-context cultures, a written agreement can be taken at face value.

2. In a high-context culture the social context surrounding the writing is far more important than the writing itself.

7.1 Become a Better Listener. Anyone can change their listening habits, but as with all habits, these changes take time and effort. Some steps are:

1. Stop talking.

2. Get rid of distractions. Distractions can be external—such as noise and movements near you, or internal—thoughts and emotions.

3. Try to enter into the speaker's reality. Try to understand where the speaker is "coming from."

4. Use pauses for reflecting. Avoid the temptation to let your mind wander.

5. Listen for main ideas.

6. Give feedback. Eye contact and facial expressions as well as responding with "I" statements are examples of feedback.

7. Listen for feelings as well as facts.

8. Encourage others to talk. This allows openness between speaker and audience, as well as clarity of the speaker's intent.

7.2 Practice High-Context Communication. Here are some rules for the higher-context countries, to use when interacting with them in conversations:

1. Recognize that people in high-context cultures need to know how to put *you* into context, to help them understand you better.

2. Try to speak as slowly and clearly as possible. Stay away from jargon, slang, clichés, and too many idioms.

3. Sprinkle your conversation with at least a few words and expressions from your listeners' native language.

4. Be careful about your nonverbal signals.

ANSWERS TO IN-CHAPTER QUESTIONS

PHOTO, page 183: Have you ever misinterpreted something that you observed? Have you ever been misinterpreted? What were the results?

Answers will vary according to students' individual experiences.

FIGURE 7.1, page 184: Who do you think plays a more important role in effective communication—the sender or the receiver?

Both play an equally important role because communication does not succeed unless the sender's message is accurately received.

PHOTO, page 186: How do you deal with information overload?

Perhaps the best way to deal with it is to eliminate any unnecessary stimuli. At home you could turn off the TV or the phone ringer, or go to another room and shut the door. At the office, you could ask to not be disturbed during certain times, or politely avoid gossip or other chatter that will distract you.

PHOTO, page 188: What are the main skills for becoming a better listener?

To becoming a better listener, stop talking and worrying about what you want to say, then try to understand where the speaker is coming from. Think about what you are hearing, both the main points and any deeper meanings. Give feedback, and encourage the speaker to say everything he or she needs to. Finally, listen for feeling as well as facts.

PHOTO, page 190: What are some possible results of filtering bad news, rather than dealing with it upfront?

Filtering makes any communication unsuccessful because the receiver isn't accepting the sender's full message. Also, filtered criticism is ignored and forgotten, even if it is constructive. Ignoring criticism may lead to increased inefficiency, accidents, or injury, and employees who choose to filter their supervisor's remarks may be fired.

FIGURE 7.2, page 192: What should you do when a speaker's verbal message does not match his or her nonverbal one?

You should listen to the nonverbal message, since this will show the speaker's true meaning (sometimes without the speaker's intent).

FIGURE 7.3, page 196: How would you interpret each gesture?

Answers will vary. Some students may interpret gestures such as the hand scissors, hand jab, and air punch as aggressive, though they can take place in a neutral conversation if they are used in a humorous way, or perhaps to discuss someone other than the receiver.

FIGURE 7.4, page 197: Which is the most common zone for you?

Most people would say the third zone, Social Distance; this is the zone you would use with coworkers, casual friends and acquaintances, and people who work with the public such as cashiers and salespeople.

FIGURE 7.5, page 201: Is the U.S. a low-context culture or a high-context culture? Why?

The U.S. tends to be a low-context culture, in which a contract or other written document can be taken as binding with no further explanation needed. High-context cultures, however, take careful consideration of nonverbal messages, cultural norms, and other atmospheric factors that are not always obvious.

PHOTO, page 202: What makes a high-context culture different from a low-context one?

High-context cultures consider all surrounding factors, while low-context cultures can take a written agreement at face value. Refer to Figure 7.5.

FIGURE 7.6, page 202: Is there any rule for doing business in other cultures?

Every culture differs, including ones that may seem similar. Americans sometimes make the mistake of assuming that all Asian (or Latin American, or Arab) countries have the same practices and beliefs, when in fact their only similarities may be quite shallow. Perhaps the best rule is: "Listen and learn."

Review Questions

1 **What is communication? In your definition, use an illustration from your own life.**

Communication can be defined as the giving and receiving of ideas, feelings, and information among people. Whatever variation of that definition students give, the illustration from the student's life can be the most telling. The best illustrations are usually of miscommunication; often they are humorous.

2 **Explain why internal climate is so important to communicating effectively. Explain the importance of self-esteem to the communication process.**

To communicate honestly and openly, both the sender and receiver need to feel good about themselves. It is primarily because of low self-esteem that people often want to talk more than listen. A good listener is usually someone who likes himself or herself enough to feel comfortable playing the less assertive role of listener. Healthy self-esteem also allows a sender to communicate without being unduly threatened by the other person. A listener with high self-esteem will be less likely to become defensive. Defensiveness is a great enemy of meaningful communication.

3 **Are you usually an active listener? If not, do you know anyone who is? What qualities set an active listener apart from other people?**

If students answer that they are usually active listeners, they have either taken training in communication, are naturally exceptional people, or are mistaken. Most likely, they are mistaken. The average adult in Western society listens with about 25 percent effectiveness.

Most people know one or more exceptional listeners who defy all of the statistics.

The qualities that set an active listener apart from other people are healthy self-esteem, ability to focus, ability to empathize, and a talent for making the other person feel important.

4 **Think of people you have been around who are poor listeners. Do they all have certain qualities in common? If so, what are they?**

Again, answers will vary.

One can usually generalize by saying that all of them put their needs above those of the other communicator. A bad listener usually lacks empathy, and empathy is really the key to active listening: to be able to ask yourself, "What would I feel like if I were this person, in this exact situation?"

Another valid point students might make would be to point out the bad habits of poor listeners. They fail to listen because they never have listened and don't really know how. Even when a student learns the material in this chapter, long months of unlearning will often be necessary, to get rid of those life-long negative listening habits.

5 **How does nonverbal communication help people understand each other? How can nonverbal cues be negative, especially in the workplace?**

Nonverbal signals are, on the whole, more reliable than their verbal counterparts. Even slight eye or body movements can convey meaning. Without nonverbals, you would be less able to convey a full message. Ask students to picture themselves talking to each other without vocal variety, gestures, or facial expressions.

Nonverbal clues are often negative. Slight changes in posture, eye contact, or vocal tone can convey feelings of power, submission, or defiance. Both managers and employees can gain a great deal of information by watching for nonverbal cues. Remind students that when the nonverbal cues contradict the verbal message, the nonverbals are to be heeded more.

6 **What are the main differences between communication in the formal organization and in the informal organization? What cautions should you use in each area?**

In the formal organization, messages are generally sent and received through formal or semi-formal channels. Timing is fairly well-ordered and somewhat predictable. The informal organization is more spontaneous and relaxed; it is also often less accurate.

Listeners must be careful in both areas to ensure that they are understanding the context of the message. When a presentation is being given in a meeting, nonverbal signals are no less important than they are in a one-on-one meeting in the informal group. Senders in both contexts need to understand the realities, prejudices, and cultural differences that might hamper clear communication.

7 **What is meant by filtering? Do you ever find yourself filtering a message being sent to you? How can one reduce the filtering of messages in the workplace?**

Filtering involves hearing only what you want to hear.

Answers will vary, but most students will admit to filtering messages.

The main trick in avoiding this trap is to tune in to reality. Notice that what you want to hear may actually be a negative message. People with low self-esteem, for example, might want to hear something negative being said about them, because their emotional state has led them to expect it.

❽ What are the major differences between a high-context culture and a low-context culture? What steps could you take when dealing with an extremely high-context culture to prevent misunderstandings?

Anthropologist Edward T. Hall has identified different cultures as being "high context" and "low context." He explains that in a low-context culture, a written agreement (such as a contract) can be taken at face value. In other words, one can assume that it means what it says and that it is in itself binding. In a high-context culture, on the other hand, the "social context" surrounding the writing is far more important than the writing itself. In other words, in a high-context culture, one must be very careful about cultural norms, nonverbal behaviors on both sides, and anything else involving the overall atmosphere of the communication. Japanese, Arab, Latin American, and Italian cultures are examples of high-context cultures. Low-context cultures include German and Scandinavian cultures. North American business culture tends to lean heavily toward the low-context end of the scale.

Obviously, the low-context cultures are not likely to cause you much trouble in communication. However, the question asks what steps one should take when encountering a high-context culture. The best answer is that you should work hard at understanding the new culture, especially in terms of how high their context really is. Impatience is one of the major frustration of Americans in dealing with higher-context cultures. Relax, take your time, and learn to understand other cultures' interpretations of concepts such as integrity and sincerity.

Critical Thinking Questions

❾ Do a brief self-evaluation. Ask yourself, "How effective a listener am I?" Were you ever guilty of poor listening? If so, what were you doing wrong? Go over the reasons for poor listening in this chapter before you reply.

Answers will vary, but the variety of questions here should help students open up.

If students recount times in which others became frustrated with their apparent lack of listening skills, but aren't sure why the frustration occurred, ask what nonverbals they were showing at that time. Were they making eye contact? Was their vocal tone varied or flat? Sometimes a person may not be guilty of poor listening, but may instead of merely *seeming* so.

❿ Think of an incident in your life when someone you were listening to was sending you nonverbal messages that seemed to contradict the verbal message. Perhaps it was a public speaker or someone on television. What was your reaction to the mixed message?

Answers will vary, but reactions can include distrust, cynicism, and frustration. If this was someone the student knew personally, ask if this affected the student's relationship with this person.

■ INTERNET EXERCISES

Tips for Teachers

1. **Nonverbal Communication** Ask students if this exercise revealed any surprises: Did the person being interviewed say anything unexpected, or was there a big difference in their verbal and nonverbal messages?

2. **Listening Skills** Ask students how this quiz (and the others on the site, if anyone tries them) influenced their self-perception in regard to listening skills. Did they learn something new about themselves? Were they initially reluctant to agree with any of the results?

Working It Out

7.1 Grapevine or Rumor Mill?

This exercise illustrates graphically how quickly distortions of fact can take place, even when communicated in a controlled environment. This exercise requires seven volunteers from the class. Six of the volunteers must immediately leave the classroom, taking their places in the hallway. This experiment will work with nearly any cooperative student, so you will be safe when allowing volunteers to come forward.

Choose the story you read carefully. Be sure it is short enough to read in 3–5 minutes, and that it contains several characters and points of detail. If the story is too simple and one-dimensional, the results won't be as dramatic. Next, have the first student retell the story to the second, the second to the third, and so on. When the last student has heard the garbled story, summarize or read the original again for the six who did not hear it in its pure form. If you have a very good reader in the class, have him or her read the story instead of doing it yourself. The student volunteers, especially those who heard the story last, will probably be surprised at the differences in interpretation. You will benefit by being only an observer of the entire process.

Working It Out

7.2 The Importance of Feedback

As mentioned in the text, this exercise illustrates the importance of two-way communication that includes feedback from all communicators. Your choice of the volunteer for this experiment is crucial. Make sure the student is fairly articulate and patient; patience is especially important during the second part of the exercise.

The volunteer from the class will study the geometrical figure at the end of this exercise. Then, with back to the class, he or she will describe the figure exactly, so that each class member can reconstruct it on a piece of notebook paper. Only the volunteer will be allowed to speak, and hand gestures are not allowed. Remember, no questions will be allowed except one request at the end to repeat each instruction.

Next, the same volunteer will *face* the class and describe the figure while classmates start over on a new sheet of notebook paper. This time, questions will be allowed.

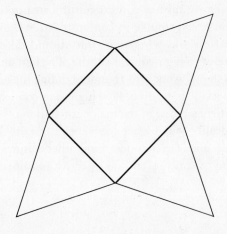

7.1 Constructive Communication

1. What is causing the central conflict in this case? Be specific.

The easiest pat answer is, of course, "Lack of communication." Try to get the students to go beyond that answer and give specifics. One could make a case for one or several of the following:

1. Stereotyping. Both project managers had "pigeonholes" in which they handily placed each other. Both men were much more complex than either had suspected of the other.

2. Poor and selective listening. Both men listened little to each other, but selectively to the negatives that were said about each other.

3. Isolation. Both men remained isolated from each other and did things that continued and encouraged further isolation.

4. Emphasizing differences rather than zeroing in on similarities. Both project managers were missing the "connectedness" that humans tend to share with one another.

5. Distrust. Neither man trusted the other enough to seek him out and find out what was really going on.

6. Weak leadership. Pete missed several opportunities to manage these two men more effectively.

2. Discuss the use (and non-use) of vertical and horizontal communication channels in this case.

The main issue is, of course, horizontal communication. These two men were equals in the company, but would not use the horizontal channels of communication available to them. Besides that, they did not even use Pete Brewer (vertical communication) to get at the issue. They simply let the situation remain until it grew intolerable. One could readily infer that negatives were communicated vertically downward by both men to their respective crews, causing more dissension and hard feelings.

3. What else could Juan Juárez do to improve the operation of the remodeling division?

Once it became known that the profit margin for remodeling had surpassed the new home division, the crews—and their managers—began to take greater pride in that accomplishment. Juárez would be wise to exploit that enthusiasm in every way possible. Also, he could meet with the two project managers on a regular basis, just to make sure that communications are staying on track. He could also use positive reinforcement to motivate the managers to keep up the new pattern of productivity.

7.2 Process the Words

1. What specific miscommunication problems caused this situation? What principles of effective communication have been broken?

Although you might be tempted to say that the vice president simply should have had a better vocabulary, it goes beyond that issue. Not everyone has a large—or, in some cases, even adequate—vocabulary. However, it is safe to say that he should have done his homework before acting, especially in so vindictive a manner, without confronting the employee. Had he done so, Sharon would undoubtedly have shown him the same dictionary definition she later relayed to him. Better yet, he should have used the dictionary himself. Sometimes, taking the time to think things through before acting can improve communication skills. The vice president not only reacted poorly to the situation, he may have embarrassed himself with his misuse of language.

2. If you had been Sharon, would you have taken any action? Why or why not?

This is an open-ended discussion question that should stimulate some interesting points of view, hopefully based on the content of chapters already covered in this course.

Some sample student reactions from classroom testing of this case include:

- "I would have quit, too. It's not the stupidity of the VP as much as the way he seemed almost hungry to fire people who offended his sensibilities."

- "I wouldn't quit. If this vice president is typical of top management, I could probably have a chance at replacing him someday soon."

- "Yes, I would have quit. If this is at all typical of the way management does things in this company, it doesn't seem like it would be too long until I really would do something that would get me fired. Might as well find a better job on my own time."

- "I would stick it out. If the vice president is a decent person at all, he'll be really careful before jumping to conclusions again."

3. Once the executive vice president realized his mistake, what should he have done, rather than officially limit the vocabulary in company memos?

He could have done several things:

1. He could have simply apologized to Sharon, explaining that the mistake was an honest one, and that if she had really been using the word he had confused with the one she used, she truly might have been an undesirable employee.

2. He could have done #1, along with enrolling in a vocabulary-building exercise or workshop for his own use. If the training proved useful, he could suggest or require it for employee training.

3. He could have issued a directive, but modified it to encourage employees who use words that might be unfamiliar to others in order to define the words in the context of their messages.

Your students will likely come up with several other possibilities.

People, Groups, and Their Leaders

LECTURE OUTLINE

I. Why Do People Join Groups?
A. A **formal group** is usually governed by the formal structure of the organization; the **informal group** simply happens. People join groups to fulfill needs that cannot be fulfilled when they act alone. Those needs—and their fulfillment—fit the following categories:
 1. Affiliation
 2. Proximity
 3. Attraction
 4. Activities
 5. Assistance
B. Groups also allow people to accomplish tasks they could never accomplish alone.

II. What Makes a Group? A **group** is defined as two or more persons who:
A. interact with other members on either an individual or network basis.
B. share most goals together.
C. are governed by unspoken or formal rules or **norms** as a system of attitudes and behaviors.
D. maintain stable role relationships.
E. form subgroups through various networks of attraction and rejection.

III. Formal Groups and Their Development. There are four distinct stages in the development of any group. All four of these stages focus on two behaviors of the group: task activity and **group process.**
A. Forming. In this stage, the group is new. Members examine their task and adjust themselves accordingly, and members begin accepting each other.
B. Redefining. Here, members learn to view the problem as a group problem. The group also tries to define itself in relation to solving this problem.
C. Coordinating. The group starts collecting information and translating it into group objectives.
D. Formalizing. The group is now at a point where it can perform meaningfully, and where it is much more likely to last.

IV. Status and Conformity in Groups
A. **Status** is the rank an individual holds within a group.
 1. Formal position in the company is one source of status.
 2. Others are factors such as interpersonal skills, personal charm or charisma, educational level, physical appearance, and persuasive ability.
 3. An important related factor is degree of *status acceptance*, or the degree to which one is accepted on the basis of his or her fulfilling status criteria.
B. **Conformity** means being willing to act in coordination and agree with the group.
C. **Groupthink** is faulty decision-making by a group that is excessively conformist. (Refer students to "Avoiding Groupthink," Figure 8.1.) Three different types of faulty thinking that stem from groupthink are:
 1. members believing too much in the great worth and status of the group.
 2. closed-mindedness.
 3. too much pressure for conformity.

V. Informal Groups. In an informal group, nobody specifically organizes the members; they just form around common interests. Although informal groups are as different from each other as the people who form them, all have some basic qualities in common:
A. They fulfill the needs of members.
B. They are necessary to the organization.
C. They are always changing.
D. They are not affected by formal boundaries.

VI. Barriers to Group Effectiveness. Some common reasons for poor group performance (and methods to remedy the problem) are:
A. ineffective norms. Most groups have never discussed their norms. Thus, examining norms is the first step.
B. identifying problems. Try to identify the problems the group is facing so that members can discuss ways to solve them.

C. composition of the group. Although changing the composition of the group is not always an option, the leader should change members to create the knowledge and skills necessary to the task.

D. hidden agendas, which are secret wishes, hopes, desires, and assumptions that members try to hide from the group. Often, people try to get these agendas accomplished even as they pretend to care about the goals of the group.

VII. Leadership: What It Is and What It Requires

A. Leadership is usually defined as the ability to influence people toward the attainment of goals.

B. Leadership versus management: According to Warren Bennis, good managers *do things right*, whereas effective leaders *do the right things*.

C. A great deal of controversy surrounds the issue of what exactly makes a leader effective.

  1. Some argue that leaders are simply born with *traits* that make them effective.

  2. Others argue that leaders have mastered different sets of *skills* anyone can develop.

  3. Still others emphasize the *situation* in which a leader finds himself or herself.

VIII. Leadership Styles. There are four styles of leadership, that will depend on the situation and personal qualities and skill level of the leader.

A. Autocratic leaders maintain control and are usually harsh on the disobedient. They can also be benevolent, expressing and dispensing kindness as long as their orders are followed.

B. Consultative leaders elicit information from followers, then make decisions based on that information. They are apt to delegate authority.

C. Participative leaders invite followers to share power with them. They regard organizational needs and group morale as equal in importance.

D. Free-rein leaders are also called *laissez-faire* leaders, a French term that means "allow them to work at will." This type allows a great deal of freedom to followers. Only a certain type of follower will allow the free-rein leader to succeed. This follower is self-directed and motivated.

E. Leaders and the Use of Power and Authority

  1. A leader's success also depends on his or her attitude toward power. Some leaders have authority, but little power.

  2. **Power** is more important than authority, because **authority** is simply one type of power—formal power.

  3. There are six main sources of power:

    a. **Legitimate power** is similar to authority because it comes from the leader's position in the organization.

    b. **Reward power** comes from the leader's ability to issue rewards, whether tangible or intangible.

    c. **Coercive power**, also known as punishment power, relies on the leader's ability to convince followers that he or she can mete out punishments.

    d. **Networking power**, or connection power, comes from "knowing the right people."

    e. **Expert power** is based on the expertise of the person who has it.

    f. **Charismatic power**, also called referent power, is based on a would-be leader's attractiveness to others.

8.1 Watching for Hidden Agendas. As either a member or leader, you can watch your own behaviors and those of group members for:

1. inappropriately strong emotions.

2. contradictions between verbal and nonverbal signals.

3. themes that keep coming up—perhaps disguised—even after the formal topic has been changed.

4. agenda conflicts that involve a member's self-esteem.

8.2 Strengthening Your Leadership Power

1. You can use the following tactics, depending on your personality and comfort zone:

  a. To strengthen your legitimate power, place yourself within an organization in a position that will give you maximum legitimate power.

  b. To strengthen your reward power, find out what the people around you value the most; then work to discover how you can reward o thers with these items or entities.

  c. To strengthen your coercive power, learn to be consistent and disciplined in your own approach to tasks and to others in the organization.

  d. To strengthen your networking power, broaden your network of friends and acquaintances.

  e. To strengthen your expert power, simply become more of an expert. Take training and management courses.

  f. To strengthen your legitimate power, stand up for others, and help them when they need help.

2. One caution: While trying to build your own power base, *don't let your ethics get out of focus.*

ANSWERS TO IN-CHAPTER QUESTIONS

PHOTO, page 215: Can you think of a time when you worked with a negative informal work group? How would you handle a situation like Julia's?

Answers will vary depending upon students' personal experiences. Students may cite several options for handling the situation, such as deciding to join the group or ignore it, quitting and leaving the company, or telling the manager.

PHOTO, page 221: How did Chris's group identify problems?

They decided to redefine their goals so that more time was spent finding out what customers wanted and how it was easiest to respond to their needs.

FIGURE 8.1, page 226: What are some of the ways in which groupthink can be reduced?

Dr. Irving Janis suggests establishing subgroups and allowing group members to freely discuss differences within the group and with the help of outside experts.

PHOTO, page 228: How can you spot people with hidden agendas?

Some obvious signs include inappropriately strong emotions and differences between a person's words and actions.

FIGURE 8.2, page 230: What style of leader would you prefer?

This depends on your type of employment and your own personality. You may need to adjust to the autocratic style of a conductor if you are playing in an orchestra, or you may enjoy the flexibility of a participative leader in a Web site design company.

PHOTO, page 234: Can networking help you strengthen other areas of power?

If you network effectively, you will have a broader knowledge of the workings of your organization, which will strengthen your expert power.

CHAPTER REVIEW, pages 240–247

Review Questions

❶ Think of groups you have joined both formally and informally. What were the benefits you expected to receive upon joining? Were those expectations fulfilled?

Although this is a personal experience question, some general conclusions are likely to come from a rather short discussion.

Benefits people want from groups tend to stay within some defined parameters. They want interaction, or affiliation: Humans are social animals, needing the company of other humans. Students also often mention finding people to do things with, since most activities that people engage in are not solo; they need others. For instance, a tennis player might want a partner to play with regularly.

Other answers will include acceptance by others with like—or even unlike—personalities, values, and points of view. Being accepted is important to people, even when self-esteem levels are high. As the text points out, people often join groups that will help them in some endeavor. On the job, groups are often formed for mutual advantage, for support and assistance in skill-building, or for help with specific projects.

❷ Recall a group to which you have belonged and identify the major norms the group followed. What were the penalties for breaking from a group norm?

Various answer will emerge. When high school groups are remembered, norms that are mentioned often involve being "cool." Although the chief taboo is doing anything that might be considered uncool, it's interesting that what is cool in one group isn't necessarily cool in another group, even in high school. Though norms vary greatly from group to group, they nearly always exist; rarely, if ever, will a normless group form. Informal groups set their norms early, and the norms often form the basis for the group's existence. Formal groups usually have formalized norms, sometimes in writing.

Students often discuss the severe penalties exacted on group members who violate an important norm. Often, the penalty is exclusion. "You do (or refuse to do) that kind of stuff, you're out of here." You might ask the class if anyone was ever in a group that had a system of punishment and reinstatement. When you find a group with a redemptive structure built into it, it is usually very worthwhile to bring it into the class discussion, especially if the group is informal.

Once a student mentioned a ham radio club he had belonged to which had as its norm the successful passing of the General Class FCC license. Until you did so, you weren't fully a member. However, one group member who had come into the group with a Novice Class license failed the General Class exam twice. When he finally passed a year later, he was reinstated to the group with full acceptance. That was a somewhat formalized redemptive structure.

❸ How did the same groups assign status in the group? What status symbols, if any, were important? Why?

Some students have mentioned groups that used cars, clothing, or both as status symbols. Others have been in groups where good grades and a high IQ were more important than material things. Still others mention groups made up only of people who are struggling financially; in this case, hardship actually took the place of a status symbol in some ways. In some classrooms, the discussion of this question may continue too long and can easily digress without close direction.

❹ The informal organization is said to help in getting work done. How does it help? How can either a manager or an employee make it help?

When people in any organization develop the attitude that the informal organization is a positive force in the workplace, amazing accomplishments can take place. For example, a supervisor wants to change a major policy or procedure in his or her sector. The supervisor identifies the informal workgroup leaders and speaks to them about the change, showing how it will help both company and employees. When the supervisor calls a meeting three days later to discuss the change, the climate is already set for acceptance because of the groundwork done in the informal organization. An employee can also use the informal group to help get work done. A network of friends can often fill in when needed. The positive spirit that the informal workgroup engenders will often become an independent force for productivity.

❺ Do groups always develop following the four steps listed in the chapter? Can you think of exceptional situations that would force groups to speed up these steps or even skip some of them?

Since groups, like individuals, are all unique, you won't need to look far to find exceptions to nearly any generalizations made about them. Review the forming, redefining, coordinating, and formalizing steps with the class; if necessary, explain each with an example. Next, give students time to trace the development of the group they are thinking about. Encourage them to take notes. Then allow volunteers to discuss their findings.

As for the second part of the question, time is an important factor. When groups are forced to form and

then perform almost immediately, the process is speeded up, and the most commonly skipped step is "redefining." Students will likely produce numerous additional examples.

❻ Do you ever watch for signs that others in a group have hidden agendas? If so, what are the signs? What can you do to confirm your suspicions?

With a little prompting, students will share hidden agendas they have observed in themselves and others. If you feel that your class needs more instruction on this topic, try the role-play in this manual at the end of this chapter: It has been classroom tested for 14 years and should work.

To discern hidden agendas, watch for repetitive behaviors on the parts of people in the group. If you are the group leader, be firm about keeping the group directly on topic. If you are a group member, watch the behavior of others closely. Remember, their hidden agendas might be totally off the topic at hand, or they could be directly related to the outcome they want from discussion of the topic. Noticing nonverbal signals can be very helpful.

To confirm your suspicions, follow up on the agenda that you suspect, doing so as subtly as possible. Of course, some group members are so adept at disguising their hidden agendas that you'll never be able to confirm your suspicions. The main point is to stop them. It's possible to know that someone has a hidden agenda without being able to discover what it is, but you can still keep that person on the topic and force objective solutions to problems.

❼ Recall a leader whose direction you once followed. Do you recognize that leader's style as autocratic, consultative, participative, or free-rein? Provide examples of behaviors that showed that style. Explain whether you liked or disliked this style of leadership.

Depending on the experience level and age of your students, this question should stimulate some interesting discussions. When students can recall extreme examples of any of the leadership styles, those are usually the most interesting and useful. Their likes and dislikes will vary.

❽ Can you imagine the same leader using more than one of the styles of leadership mentioned in question #7? Would this improve their abilities as a leader? How can flexibility influence a leader? Are there any drawbacks to flexibility?

"Can you imagine" questions are quite open-ended. The fact is that the same manager could feasibly use all four of these styles. Usually, the issue is the nature of the situation. Also, very often the most crucial factor in the situation will be the needs and proclivities of the followers. If a leader has what leadership scholar Warren Bennis calls "leadership flexibility," he or she should be able to adapt to the maturity and skill level of the employee to use the style most appropriate.

Perceived unfairness is an important issue that often arises in the course of a discussion of a question such as this is. When an employee sees a manager treating another employee in a totally different manner, the employee often suspects that the manager is being unfair or arbitrary. To prevent that unfortunate by-product of flexibility requires some genuine leadership skill. Class discussion can produce some interesting answers to this issue.

Critical Thinking Questions

9 **Which of the leadership styles is yours or would most likely be yours? Why did you choose this particular style? Does your profession of choice match with this style? How does this leadership style reflect your personality?**

The most important part of this question is "Why?" A typical answer such as "Because that's what I would feel the most comfortable with" is not deep enough. Students should understand that different careers have different styles of leadership. Try following that sort of answer up with "What kind of employee are you imagining (or have you already managed) when you are choosing that style?" Another follow-up question is "Would you be able to change your style of leadership if your followers—or something else crucial to the situation—changed suddenly?" Still another would be "If you were the ideal person what leadership style would you prefer in most situations? (Refer students back to the ideal self in Chapter 2.)"

Answers will vary depending on students' preferences.

10 **Which of the six sources of power do you consider to be the strongest in most cases? Which of them would you be the most likely to develop and use? Why? Which of the six sources of power do you consider the least important? Why?**

This question works in the classroom only when the students have a thorough understanding of all six sources. Answers will vary widely, of course. The main issue is to draw out from the students their thorough understanding of what each source is and how to acquire and build it.

Answers will vary depending on students' preferences.

Working It Out

8.1 Group Cohesiveness

This experiment should be thoroughly understood by participants before beginning. Students might be told to read the instructions over before class to be sure they all understand. The class should be given about 20 minutes to arrive at a consensus. Be sure the concept of consensus decision-making is understood by everyone before they begin.

Key for Survey Score Column

1. Pleasant working conditions	14
2. Fair wages and fringe benefits	8
3. Appreciation from management	4
4. Ability to advance in company	3
5. Loyalty of company to employees	10
6. Adequate vacation time	15
7. Help with work problems	12
8. Help with personal problems	13
9. Meaningful work	1
10. Involvement in decision-making	2
11. Security from layoffs	9
12. Skillful and fair discipline	11
13. Being informed of company plans	7
14. Being involved in change efforts	6
15. Working without interference	5

If you don't want to use the list in the group exercise, it can be a stimulating source for discussion on its own. What are the top five? The bottom five? Does the whole class agree?

Working It Out

8.2 Quality of Work Life

This exercise works nicely as a homework assignment, and can also be used as a combination homework-group exercise. After the students have created their lists at home, they can form groups and attempt to reach a consensus on what are the most important qualities for any group to have.

INTERNET EXERCISES

Tips for Teachers

1. **Self-Assessment** Any of the tests in the "Bias, Prejudice, and Attitudes" section are helpful, so you may prefer to let students take the test or tests of their choosing.

2. **Apply** Nearly all of the exercises at this Web site are fun, and students could easily be distracted. Reiterate to them that at least one of the exercises they engage in must focus on groups and leaders.

Case Study

8.1 Making Foreman at Somar

1. Describe the informal work group that Henry was a part of.

This group's norms require disdaining authority and valuing attractive automobiles; in fact, the status symbols that were valued the most were their cars. Thus, Henry broke the norms by not caring about cars and by showing himself to be an aspiring supervisor.

2. What could the managers at Somar do to change this destructive mentality?

Whatever they do, they will have to affect the basic culture of their workforce. That is rarely easy. Possibilities include:

- altering their hiring policies to ensure that all new hires are accepting and inclusive people. In a time of prosperity, however, this might not be an option, especially with employee shortages that affect the construction field during such times.
- example-setting by management.
- training in human relations, which has been used in construction companies with some real success.

Class discussion should bring up a few more suggestions.

3. Evaluate Henry's situation in terms of norms and status.

He cannot both meet the norms of the group and remain himself. Although he could buy the "right" kind of car, his attitude toward this status symbol would likely negate the power of the symbol. In short, he would be forced to pretend that attractive cars were considerably more important in his hierarchy of values than they could ever be. As a supervisor, Henry can possibly rise above the stigmas of the past. However, he doesn't share the group norms. His only chance is to change the current group norms through open communication.

Case Study

8.2 Cleaning Up Ace Furniture

1. What leadership style does Gina seem to be using?

Most students will say autocratic. She seems arbitrary and not thoughtful of the feelings of the employees, even though she senses that they resent her because of her gender. You might ask the class if they think the resentment includes more than gender prejudice.

2. What are Gina's sources of power? Are these the ones she should be using?

First, she is obviously using legitimate power. She relies on her position in the company as a point of departure for her arbitrary orders and relies on it heavily. This is a type of position power. She also uses a certain amount of coercive power. She seems to feel that she needs to call upon coercion to enforce her orders. Again, as mentioned in the text, this is a type of position power.

Since she relies only on these two power sources, both of which are position based, she can be seen as being in a relatively weak power position.

3. If you were Gina's manager, would you try to change behaviors in her leadership methods? Which ones? Why?

Students should say that she needs to broaden her power base. She has very little power, simply because she doesn't understand where power really comes from—the support of followers. Because she has little or no support, she needs to develop the power sources that will best give her that very important leadership element.

Also, some students might mention that Gina is apparently following a male role model as a leader. You might ask your class what they think of that possibility. If it's true, Gina is making a very common mistake made by female leaders: following a highly aggressive role model is usually a bad idea for men or women. A good, constructive discussion can develop from this point.

Teams in Quality Organizations

LECTURE OUTLINE

I. Quality Organizations: Total Quality Management (TQM) is an organizational philosophy that says that quality must be present in goods, services, and all related support activities.

   A. TQM emphasizes **empowerment** of employees and **rewards** for attaining higher quality in goods and processes.

   B. W. Edwards Deming is credited with putting together 14 points for a successful TQM program.

     1. Deming's work was most influential in Japan, but TQM is now also in the U.S.

     2. TQM creates loyalty and commitment to the organization, and increased self-confidence and self-esteem in employees.

     3. TQM relies on teams and group work.

II. Team Building

   A. Work teams are created by managers to achieve group goals. Work teams take time and effort to set up, but increase productivity overall.

   B. Team spirit allows the group to work toward the group's success. This idea is counter to traditional management, which includes a boss giving orders to employees.

   C. Building a team includes the following ideas:

     1. Implementation can begin when the team builder (often a consultant) asks members of the work group what they want from the team, how the team will benefit them, and what they have to offer the work team.

     2. Trust is an essential element of team building.

     3. The work team must agree on goals, both individually and collectively.

   D. The stages in team building are alternatively described as:

     1. forming, when the team mission is finalized.

     2. storming, when group conflicts arise and are resolved.

     3. norming, when rules are set and the group gets down to business.

     4. performing, when the team works hard and completes the project.

III. Decision Making in Teams. There are several factors that influence who will make the decisions in a group, including: time pressure, importance of decision quality, group acceptance of the decision, expertise and philosophy of managers, and potential for group conflict. Possible decision-making models include:

   A. Minority. One person or a few group members make the decisions.

   B. Majority. More than half the group decides.

   C. Unanimous. All team members must agree on the decision.

   D. Consensus. All team members agree to carry out the decision, even if all do not agree on what the decision was.

IV. Organizational Climate: The Weather of the Workplace

   A. Organizational climate is like weather: It is described as warm or cold, can change quickly, and is influenced by environmental factors.

   B. Major qualities of organizational climate:

     1. It reflects employees' desire for trust, recognition, freedom to be creative, fairness, and independence.

     2. It is produced by relationships between employees.

     3. It reflects the organization's culture.

     4. It influences its employees' behavior.

     5. It helps in understanding situations in the organization.

   C. Climates can be autocratic, participative, or chaotic. A good climate encourages long-term productivity.

V. Corporate Culture: Shared Values. Corporate culture is the network of shared values of varying importance. These cultures can be good, bad, or mixed.

A. **Culture stories** are the oral history that preserve each corporate culture.

VI. **Types of Corporate Culture.** Five types of corporate culture are described by Poupart and Hobbs of the University of Quebec.

    A. Father-founder culture. The same person who founded the company still runs it. It is usually a centralized operation.

    B. Bureaucratic culture. This company's culture is formal, predictable, and aims for efficiency.

    C. Participative culture. This company's culture emphasizes group work and cooperation.

    D. Professional culture. This culture is based on expertise, and developing skills and knowledge.

    E. Managerial-entrepreneurial culture. This culture centers around an adventurous spirit, productivity, and customer satisfaction.

VII. **The "New" Corporate Culture: The Importance of Self-Esteem**

    A. Current thoughts are that the most productive corporate cultures enhance the self-esteem of employees.

    B. Managers should not bully or intimidate employees, which is the autocratic approach.

VIII. **The Importance of Fairness.** Fairness is very important. Trust, consistency of treatment, truthfulness, integrity, open expectations, equity, influence allowed to all employees, justice, respect, and overall fairness are important aspects to consider in the **psychological contract** between employees and employers.

    A. Participative management should be encouraged.

    B. Self-esteem development among all members of the organization is encouraged.

    C. The corporate culture is goal-oriented.

9.1 Building a Successful Team

1. Train the team.
2. Manage the team as a team.
3. Delegate authority specifically.
4. Be a clarifier.
5. Be a communicator.

9.2 Changing Your Workplace Climate

1. Check your own example.
2. Listen to your colleagues.
3. Notice physical details.
4. Get rid of ambiguity.
5. Make people feel important.

9.3 Creating Fairness in the Workplace

1. Maintain trust at work.
2. Create consistency at work.
3. Expect truthfulness at work.
4. Maintain integrity from yourself and employees.
5. Create expectations for employees.
6. Treat everyone with the same rules.
7. Allow employees to have influence in decisions.
8. Administer appropriate rewards and discipline.
9. Create a corporate culture of overall fairness.

ANSWERS TO IN-CHAPTER QUESTIONS

PHOTO, page 251: Can you think of a time when a supervisor thought he or she was creating a team environment, but was actually doing the exact opposite?

Students' answers will vary depending on experiences.

PHOTO, page 253: How would you improve training at the job where you currently work, or at the workplace of someone you know?

Many people state that their employers do not provide enough training, or that it does not contain enough hands-on experience to prepare them adequately for their jobs.

FIGURE 9.1, page 254: Which of these guidelines seems most important?

Your answer will depend on what you consider most important for a company's success: For example, it could be strong leadership, comprehensive training, or company-sponsored educational programs.

FIGURE 9.2, page 258: What factors need to be in place for effective teamwork?

Teams need to have a clear understanding of the task at hand (determined during the first two stages), as well as the ability to work together with minimal conflict (which was hopefully resolved during the second stage).

PHOTO, page 260: What do you look for in an organization's climate?

Answers will vary.

FIGURE 9.3, page 265: If you were to start your own business, which type of corporate culture would you foster?

Your answer will depend on your ability to motivate, on the personalities of those you will hire, and on the type of business itself.

PHOTO, page 268: How does participative management help employees feel wanted and respected at their jobs?

By encouraging participative management, an organization sends a clear signal that employee feedback is helpful and should be recognized. When employees feel that their contributions are appreciated, their self-esteem and interest in their jobs flourish.

FIGURE 9.4, page 269: Which factor do you consider most important?

Many people will answer that many or all of these factors are equally important, or that they are interdependent (i.e., truthfulness is necessary for integrity and trust).

PHOTO, page 271: What happens when this contract is broken?

By breaking the psychological contract, managers can make employees feel betrayed and distrustful of the organization. Saying that an unfulfilled agreement "wasn't in writing" is not an adequate excuse, for a manager's word should be trustworthy.

PHOTO, page 273: Can you think of any other steps to enhance team building?

Answers will vary.

CHAPTER REVIEW, pages 278–284

Review Questions

❶ **Think of an ideal version, in your opinion, of a perfect organizational climate. What characteristics would be included?**

This question urges students to create their own workplace utopia. Many of the utopian characteristics will be universally agreed upon. First, management would be kind and open to new suggestions, readily available for solving problems and offering support, and efficient but not authoritarian. Second, individual talents and abilities would be utilized to the maximum. Everyone would be allowed to work with minimal interference from management, who would offer help only when needed. Third, the physical environment would be conducive to work—no garish colors, drafty floors, or cramped quarters.

❷ **Fairness is an important quality of a positive, or warm, organizational climate and culture. What qualities are necessary for a perception of fairness to exist throughout an organization?**

Whatever else students come up with, their answers should include trust, consistency, truthfulness, integrity, clear expectations, equity, justice, and mutual respect. In discussion, you can point out that a perception of fairness is not exactly the same as the reality of fairness. In other words, management must both communicate fairness and practice it simultaneously. This is because fairness is a central issue in the psychological contract between manager and employee.

❸ Explain the "New Corporate Culture." In your opinion, would this type of culture lead toward success for America as an international competitor? Why or why not?

The new corporate culture is based on norms that make an organization more humane, closely-knit, profitable, and productive. It is based on a new set of assumptions about how people should be treated in the workplace. In the new corporate culture, managers should not bully or intimidate employees, which is the old autocratic approach. The new corporate culture is goal-oriented.

Most students will say that this type of corporate culture will help the U.S. to become a successful international competitor because its values enhance productivity and employee satisfaction.

❹ At a recent national conference attended by one of your authors, a facilitator introduced a workshop topic as "How to Work In Teams and Other Morale-Raising Crap." The audience's reaction was one of surprise at the speaker's negativity toward the announced topic. Based on information from this chapter, what type of corporate culture would you guess this facilitator worked in? How well does it fit with the "new" corporate culture?

The facilitator probably worked in a bureaucratic culture that emphasizes formality, cost efficiency, and following procedures. Since team-building and morale-building exercises are typically not seen by this culture as being important to the legal and rational aspects of a business, they would probably not be emphasized or implemented. The facilitator may have worked in a professional culture, which emphasizes expertise, skills, knowledge, and the power of the intellect. Also, this type of culture does not focus on team-building or morale-building in an organization.

Some father-founder cultures, depending on the experience and personality of the founder, may see the advantages of team-building and morale-building. Participative cultures may see the benefits, too, as might managerial-entrepreneurial cultures.

❺ Think about each of the types of corporate culture described in this chapter: father-founder, bureaucratic, participative, professional, and managerial-entrepreneurial. Which type would you prefer to work in? If you had your own company, which type of culture would you create?

Answers will vary, based on the student's preference. Many students will say they don't like any of the models, and would rather create a new corporate culture company. Students who do select one of the five types of corporate culture listed above should be able to describe it.

❻ What are the advantages of working in teams rather than individually? What are the advantages of developing a team spirit? Do you feel a team spirit where you work (or where you would like to work, in the ideal)?

Teamwork allows people to learn information from several viewpoints rather than just one. It can be a more efficient process if tasks are assigned based on skills and interests, and if the team functions as a sort of production line rather than having one person perform all tasks of a single project.

A team spirit helps to develop loyalty and commitment to the organization. Employees have better attitudes and are more productive.

Some students will say they feel a team spirit and others will not, but most will say they would prefer to work in a place that has a team spirit.

❼ Look over Deming's 14 points for quality. In your opinion, which three would be the easiest to implement? Why? Which three would be the most difficult to implement? Why?

Points that are objective, easily measured, and call for cessation of an activity will be easiest to implement, such as abandoning slogans, ending dependence on mass inspection, eliminating financial goals and quotas, no longer awarding business based solely on the basis of price, and eliminating annual ratings. These are easiest because they involve stopping a behavior.

The most difficult points to implement will be those that call for global change across the organization, in abstract terms. These would include instituting leadership, driving out fear, constantly improving every system, adopting the new philosophy of quality in its entirety, and structuring management to accomplish this transformation. These are difficult to institute because they are somewhat abstract, call for beginning a behavior rather than ceasing one, and offer no clear direction as to how to attain this objective.

❽ Imagine yourself as (a) a ship captain, and (b) a football team captain. What are the advantages and disadvantages of each? Considering these advantages and disadvantages, why do you suppose that the team captain, rather than the ship captain, is a more popular analogy for management styles today in the U.S.?

The advantage of being the ship captain is that there is only one leader, and the leader gets things done quickly without having to allow others into the decision-making process. Since the decision is autocratic, it is always the decision the ship captain wanted. A disadvantage is that there is only one viewpoint considered, and it might not be the right one. A ship captain is also more likely to inspire mutiny than a football captain because of the autocratic nature of the decision-making process.

A football team captain, on the other hand, must consider the abilities, talents, skills, and needs of the team members. Decisions are not made in isolation, since the team must work together to attain its goals. This team approach defines the advantages of this process. The disadvantages are that it takes longer to come to decisions when others are involved in the process, the final decision might not be the one the captain wanted to make, and there is more chance for conflict among team members when they all have a voice.

Critical Thinking Questions

9 One of TQM's areas of emphasis is empowerment, or giving employees decision-making power in their work-related problems and goals. After reading this chapter, do you think this is a good idea? Why or why not? Is it possible to give employees too much power? Is there a downside to giving employees power? In your ideal work setting, how much power would you have?

Answers will vary. Most students will say that empowerment is always a good idea. Students who are thinking as managers may say that giving employees too much power dilutes the quality of the company or product. Some students may refer back to Theory X and say that many employees do not want power, so in that case giving it to them is a bad idea.

10 In the mini-history of TQM, you learned that businesses in the U.S. did not accept Deming's ideas until much later than businesses in Japan. What is it about the traditional corporate culture in the U.S. that could explain this? How would the business history of the U.S. have changed if businesses had accepted Deming's ideas early on?

Answers will vary. Corporate culture in the U.S. has not traditionally favored the concepts of groups and teams, which may have contributed to the slow acceptance of this philosophy in the U.S. In addition, a traditional corporate culture that has been in place a long time with satisfactory rates of success may not seem to need change. Perhaps managers are slow to change a system that seems to be working: the philosophy of "If it ain't broke, don't fix it." Traditional American corporate culture does not foster a strong sense of loyalty and commitment to one's company or workplace, as has been the case in Japan and is the case with TQM.

If the TQM philosophy had been accepted earlier in the U.S., there would be more businesses and corporations relying on teamwork. Perhaps people would work in the same company for years, or for life. The concepts of empowerment and rewards would not be new and would

perhaps have found their way into mainstream culture, changing the way people teach students, raise children, and relate to one another. There would probably be a higher quality of goods and services in all sectors, and as consumers we would have come to expect that in all situations.

Working It Out

9.1 How is the "Weather" in Your Organizational Climate?

Students typically have fun with this assignment. Many will analyze professors' offices, including your own—so be prepared to see your office from a student's (perhaps unflattering) perspective.

Students typically describe warm offices as those with personal pictures or visible personal effects, plants, with little distance and few furnishings separating students from the office resident. Offices that are overly cluttered or disorganized, and those that are stark and bare, are described as cold. Nonverbal communication that is appropriate and friendly is described as warm.

Working It Out

9.2 Role-Play

This activity usually works well during a short class period, especially with students who are enthusiastic about role-playing serving as team leaders. Students can take this activity further by improvising even worse, and then better, scenarios and dialogue.

INTERNET EXERCISES

Tips for Teachers

1. **Read and Summarize** Encourage students to find opposing viewpoints on coaching and then ask them which coaching ideas did *not* resonate with them. Why?

2. **Self-Assessment** After students complete this exercise, ask them how an individual can build team spirit from scratch, especially in organizations that are lacking it.

9.1 Selling TQM?

1. What does Seth mean by asking Tom to just consider the product and not the process? How does this relate to TQM?

Seth is asking Tom to ignore the process by which the department and the old sheriff got things done—presumably at the expense of civil rights of accused lawbreakers. In the old sheriff's traditional management style, there was no day-to-day accountability required of the staff. Seth apparently liked it that way.

TQM relates well to this example because TQM demands quality in all aspects of the operation of a company, regardless of the product of the organization. Traditional management just looks at the quality of the end product, ignoring the process.

2. Does this type of organization technically "fit" with TQM's purpose? Is Tom right when he describes the products and the clients involved?

This type of organization is probably not what Deming had in mind when thinking about goods and services, but the TQM points are certainly relevant. Tom's description of community members as clients is appropriate, and upholding the law is an appropriate description of the product or service being provided by the sheriff's department.

3. What differences do you think will occur in this small law enforcement agency with the implementation of TQM? Explain your answer.

If Tom's new management style is implemented and accepted by the staff and the community, then we would expect to see changes for the better in the areas of community relations (customer satisfaction) and improvement of the law enforcement process (overall organization quality). We would expect fewer citizen complaints as evidence of higher customer satisfaction, and fewer civil rights violations as evidence of improved overall quality. Since staff members will be thinking of themselves as members of a team rather than as individual "vigilantes," they should not feel resentment toward Tom after TQM is implemented. Their attitudes, loyalty, commitment, and overall job satisfaction will likely improve.

9.2 Alone on Her Team

1. Is Ken right—does the new insurance company president have good ideas? If so, what are they? If not, then what is his motivation for the restructuring?

Ken appears to be right, and the new president does appear to have some good ideas.

The new president sounds as though he is trying to institute work teams and perhaps TQM to encourage cooperation and increase productivity. These are good ideas since they tend to increase individual work satisfaction and overall corporate productivity.

The new president's motivation probably comes from those advantages of work teams.

2. Suppose you are the new president of the insurance company, and Nikki comes to your office to complain about how stupid she thinks the new restructuring plans are. What will you say to persuade her otherwise?

You could ask her to give the work teams a try before deciding the restructuring is stupid. You could say that work teams usually result in more satisfied employees who have better attitudes toward their jobs. You could also tell her that when working in a team, she will probably be able to focus more on particular tasks that match her skills and interests, while other tasks that she is less interested in could be shared by other team members.

3. What type of corporate culture does it sound like the new insurance company president is trying to instill? (If you can't tell from the information given, what are your guesses?) What can you guess about the intended organizational climate?

This sounds like the new corporate culture, or the team culture that is promoted by TQM. It may be a participative culture or a managerial-entrepreneur culture that has built in a teamwork component. The focus on team building is most likely one of those, since the other types of cultures described (father-founder, bureaucratic, professional) fit less well with the work team concept.

The intended organizational climate is warm and stable.

Transactions and Relationships

LECTURE OUTLINE

I. Transactional Analysis

A. Transactional analysis deals with emotions, motivations, and feelings that are deeply rooted in the unconscious mind. Much of the brain's function takes place in the **unconscious mind**. Most psychologists agree that personality is controlled by the unconscious.

B. Dr. Eric Berne found that the brain behaves like a two-track tape recorder, one track remembering things that happened, the other recording the emotions and feelings connected with what happened.

C. A **transaction** is any exchange of words between two people. When you see each person in the transaction behaving as a parent, an adult, and a child, you can analyze the transaction with a diagram.

II. Transactional Analysis as a Whole System

A. For this, people use the term transactional analysis (or TA). TA is a whole system of psychology created specifically for everyday people.

B. However, most TA specialists warn against using the knowledge you will gain here to practice informal therapy or for any other purpose that could be potentially damaging to another person

III. Three People Types: Child, Parent, and Adult. There are three "people types" within everyone, known as the parent, adult, and child **ego states**. They exist because people's unconscious "tapes" have recorded them as the three major forces in their lives as they were growing up.

A. The **child ego state** is divided into three parts, representing three types of childlike behavior:

1. The **natural child** contains all of the happiness, imagination, openness, and warmth of childhood.

2. The **adapted child** has "adapted" to a parent figure. Children adapt themselves to fit whatever parent figure with whom they are reacting.

3. The **little professor** is notable for intuition, creativity, and manipulation.

B. The **parent ego state** has two main functions. First, it allows the individual to do well as parent. Second, it allows for automatic responses without consulting one's adult ego state.

1. The **critical parent** replays the criticism, the put-downs, and the "do's" and "don'ts" your parents taught you.

2. The **sympathetic parent** ego state calls up a sympathetic, nurturing parent figure somewhere in the past. The sympathetic parent allows you to be protective and helpful to others.

C. The **adult ego state** involves rational, unemotional, and careful thinking and analyzing, without letting emotions get in the way.

D. Recognizing the ego states. Once you have identified these parts of your own personality, you will also be able to see them in others. Some people have favorite ego states and will stay in one much more than in the others.

IV. Transaction Types. Just as there are three basic ego states, there are three types of transactions: complementary, crossed, and ulterior. The type of transaction depends not only on the content of the message, but on nonverbal signals as well.

A. Complementary transactions. When the message you send to the other person gets a response that is close to the one you expected, a complementary transaction has taken place.

B. Crossed transactions happen when you receive responses you did not expect. Communication is broken off when a crossed transaction takes place.

C. Ulterior transactions take place on two levels at the same time. One transaction is open and obvious, while the other hidden one is the real, genuine intention of the conversation.

D. Third move transactions are second chances to form meaningful transactions. In a third move transaction, the one who speaks last is the one who determines the way the transaction turns out.

1. Changing ego states. To invite the first speaker to move to the *adult* ego state:
   a. Ask a question.
   b. Make an adult statement. State facts unemotionally.
   c. Ask for options and for the other person's preference.
2. To invite a person to move to the *sympathetic parent* ego state:
   a. Ask for help.
   b. Communicate your fears about the situation (if you have them) to the other person.
   c. Ask for advice.
3. To invite a person to move to the *natural child*:
   a. Be yourself—assuming that you have a sense of humor.
   b. Show the fun and interesting sides of the situation.
   c. Be a sympathetic parent. Say, "I'd like to help."
   d. Be enthusiastic; share your excitement with the other person.
   e. Show a new or fresh way of looking at old things.

V. Scripts

A. People's transactions are based on scripts they heard as children. **Scripts** come from nearly all human influences that affect the first years of childhood. Some types of scripts are:
   1. Cultural scripts, which originate in your cultural background.
   2. Family scripts, which originate in family lessons from childhood.
   3. Religious scripts, which are usually tied in with family scripts, since religious scripting, if any, nearly always comes from one's family.
   4. Gender scripts: Both family and cultural influences help people form their scripts about what is acceptable conduct for males and females.

B. No matter which of the four categories a script belongs to, each will fit into one of the following script concepts:
   1. Commands
   2. Counter-commands
   3. Permission scripts
   4. Mythical hero scripts

VI. Life Positions. Besides your scripts, you are also caught in one of four **life positions**:
   A. I'm not OK—you're OK. Sadly, this is the most popular life position.
   B. I'm not OK—you're not OK. This life position is one

of despair. The person who stays in this position into later life has a very hard time with relationships.
   C. I'm OK—you're not OK. This is the life position of many habitual criminals. The "I'm OK" part of the position is actually a lifesaving choice. Other people seem not OK because of the unfair way people in this life position were often treated as children. These victims of childhood unfairness are "OK" because they have to be—otherwise there would be no reason to go on.
   D. I'm OK—you're OK. Unlike the other life positions, this one is chosen consciously. To like and accept yourself totally, you also must accept others completely. Do not expect to remain in this chosen ego state constantly, however. Most people have periods of time when they slip into one of the other positions temporarily.

VII. Strokes and Stroking

A. **Stroking** is anything one person does to recognize the accomplishments and worth of another. The amount of stroking you need or yearn for seems to have a relationship to the number of strokes you received as a child.
   B. Stroking needs to be kept in balance.
   1. When people fall below their "comfort zone" of strokes, they will usually become depressed.
   2. When too much attention is paid and too many strokes are given, the person will also suffer from stress and will need to escape.

VIII. Games People Play. A **game** is an ongoing series of complementary ulterior transactions. Workplace games are usually unreasonable, emotion-based activities that deal badly with real-life situations and do not help any of the players.

IX. Assertiveness Versus Aggressiveness. Assertiveness means standing up for one's own rights without violating others. **Aggressiveness** means going too far, to the point of threatening others' self-esteem and putting them on the defensive. This distinction is important in the application of transactional analysis.

 10.1 Stopping Games Before They Start. The best way to become aware of games and the people who play them is to watch for conversations and events that happen repeatedly. Here are some tips on stopping games before you get hooked into them:

1. Work on your self-esteem.
2. Try to stay in the adult ego state.
3. Hook the other person's adult ego state.
4. Give and receive positive strokes.
5. De-emphasize the weaknesses of others.

ANSWERS TO IN-CHAPTER QUESTIONS

PHOTO, page 287: What were some different ways Carmen could have responded to the salesperson? What would you have done?

Answers will vary. However, transactional analysis may help conflicts as they occur. Using this process to study transactions, or conversations, with other people will allow you to deal with a difficult exchange.

FIGURE 10.1, page 290: Can you control your mind's stimulus response?

Yes. By understanding your reactions and those of other people, you will be able to teach yourself to change your reactions into ones that will benefit you more.

PHOTO, page 291: How can adults enjoy the natural child ego state?

You enjoy this state in creative activities like art or dance, in learning experiences, and when you are just relaxing and having fun. The natural child should never be outgrown!

FIGURE 10.2, page 295: Which state do you find yourself in most often?

Answers will vary, but many people do not spend most of their time in the adult ego state. If you find that your life is rather carefree, you may identify with the natural child; if you find that you are constantly controlling people who do not live up to your expectations, you may be playing the critical parent role.

FIGURE 10.3, page 296: What are the characteristics of this type of transaction?

In this type of transaction, both sender and receiver are showing rational, unemotional, and careful thinking. Since this is a complementary transaction, the sender understands the receiver's intended message.

FIGURE 10.4, page 297: What are some examples of parent–child complementary transactions?

One common example is the critical parent/adapted child transaction, where one person is critical to another person, who appears remorseful and "adapts" to the other's wishes. Another is the sympathetic parent/natural child, in which one person offers nurturing and guidance to another person, who feels comfortable enough to open up and show childlike vulnerability.

PHOTO, page 298: How can you make more of your transactions complementary?

To make more of your transactions complementary, listen carefully, watch for nonverbal signals, and ask questions about what is being said. If you are the one speaking, ask for feedback.

FIGURE 10.5, page 299: How can you change a crossed transaction to a complementary one?

You can try several different approaches. First of all, you must re-initiate the transaction, for a crossed transaction is one that has been broken off. You can either meet the other person at the level they want, or you can try to get them to meet your ego state.

FIGURE 10.6, page 301: What do nonverbal signals tell you about ulterior transactions?

Nonverbal signals can help you decipher the true meaning of an ulterior transaction. Notice the other speaker's tone of voice, facial expressions, eye contact, and body movements. Sometimes, though, an ulterior message is so subtle that even nonverbal clues won't help.

PHOTO, page 305: How can you rewrite your own scripts?

The important thing is to remember that you can rewrite any script. The important question is whether it will improve your life and make you happier. Learning to understand what scripts are and how they work will enable you to rewrite them.

FIGURE 10.7, page 307: Which life position is the healthiest and happiest?

The "I'm OK, You're OK" life position is by far the healthiest and happiest. This is also the only one that is chosen consciously; the other three are by-products of unhappy experiences.

PHOTO, page 310: What happens when someone receives too many or too few strokes?

Too many strokes can make a person feel suffocated, and can have a negative effect; always be careful that you are not bestowing too much positive reinforcement on someone. Too few strokes, however, can lead to lowered self-esteem and even physical illness.

PHOTO, page 314: How can you stop games as soon as you detect them?

Do not let your own self-esteem falter because of someone else's manipulation. Stay in the adult ego state, and try to encourage the gameplayer to join you in it. Stroke the gameplayer in a sincere, open way that will disarm him or her. Finally, do not give in to the urge to manipulate a gameplayer in return.

Review Questions

❶ Briefly explain the characteristics of the adult ego state. How much time do you spend in the adult? Are you in the adult more at work than you are at home or when involved in social activities? Explain.

The adult ego state is detached, unemotional, and analytical. Its use involves careful, fact-based thinking that takes notice of as many sides of an issue as possible. Emotions do not get in the way of this sort of rational thinking.

Answers to the second part of the question will vary because of both individual differences and differing levels of honesty. Many traditional-age college students spend a great deal of time in the child ego state, which is certainly not to be condemned. As someone has said, "If you can't act like a kid when you are a kid, when can you?" Nearly any student who is quite serious about a college career, though, must spend a certain amount of time in the adult ego state. Just how much time will often depend on the course being pursued and the tolerance of the professor and fellow students.

Many people of all ages spend a large percentage of leisure hours (when they have them) in the natural child ego state. The view from the 1960s, which held that people should always be in the natural child, is no less unbalanced than the 1980s approach that overemphasized the adult. Even in the workplace, where the adult ego certainly should predominate, balance is important. Today, where TA is still taught, it is taught in a balanced manner, with adult–adult complementary important in the workplace, but never to be used exclusively. (See question #3.)

❷ What types of situations or conditions might make it difficult for many people in business to use their adult ego state? How can these problems be overcome?

Students might mention any number of workplace realities based on their own experiences:

1. The parental attitude of many traditional managers. If you are a manager and your only mentor or role model was a parental type, you must fight the conditioned tendency to act parentally as a manager.
2. The automatic response by employees to parental managers. If a manager is sending a parental stimulus to you, unless you are really thinking about your reaction, it is likely to come from the child ego state.
3. The angry customer. The angry customer is likely to be coming from either the adapted child or the critical parent, sometimes fluctuating between the two. The businessperson must concentrate on the results that are required from the situation, rather than letting the customer stimulus produce a destructive response. (Chapter 15, "Customers and Your Company Image," deals with this issue in non-TA terms.)
4. The gossiping coworker. Gossip is usually based on some type of child–child or parent–parent complementary transaction. (That is, unless the gossip is passed to an unreceptive receiver.) Playful gossip can remain totally in the natural child, but vicious and destructive gossip is probably coming from the critical parent. Sympathetic parent could be something like:

"Poor dear, she seems to have a real drinking problem!"

"Yes, poor thing, something really needs to be done."

Although these four situations are the most common, students will invariably come up with excellent examples to augment them. The gossip trap is very easy to fall into and, contrary to popular notions, men do it at least as much as women. Also, managers have been known to fall into this trap as both receivers and senders.

❸ Providing at least two examples, explain why adult–adult complementary is usually the best transaction in a business setting.

When you discard the child and parent scripts and dwell in the adult, you tend to be more objective, problem-oriented, and focused. In business, problems—especially people problems—often have emotional overtones. In the adult ego state, it is possible to work above those emotions and reach realistic solutions based on facts and reason. There are workplace situations wherein the adult ego state might be less effective than, say, the sympathetic parent. For example, a frightened and upset customer might need some parental calming down before the adult ego state takes care of the remedy. This is why the adult–adult complementary transaction is usually the appropriate choice for the workplace.

Another example is the manager–employee relationship wherein the manager insists on staying in the critical parent. The employee's best procedure is to continue to cause a crossed transaction by replying in the adult. In many cases, this practice will eventually force the manager into the adult, resulting in adult–adult complementary.

The best student examples are usually from their own experiences.

4   Explain the little professor ego state. What signals can warn you that a little professor is manipulating you? How can you avoid falling into this ego state yourself?

The little professor ego state is explained best in James and Jongeward's *Born to Win*. The authors explain that parts of both the natural child and the adapted child come together to form a third, very manipulative ego state.

Whenever you feel that your "buttons are being pushed" or you are being taken advantage of in any other way, it is likely that you are being manipulated by a little professor.

For people who grew up as manipulators, avoiding this trap might be more difficult than it sounds. The would-be little professor should stop and ask, "Am I being straightforward with this person in this transaction? Do I have a hidden agenda, or am I engaged in honest self-disclosure?"

5   Explain why a crossed transaction usually ends a conversation. What can either person do to start the transaction again?

The simplest explanation is that the initiator of the transaction is receiving an unexpected response. This surprise element destroys the rhythm of the transaction. Let's say that Frank, the manager, says to John, his employee, "You'd better have that report for me first thing tomorrow, or I'll have your hide!" in a harsh, superior tone. John simply replies, in a matter-of-fact tone, "I have exactly five hours of working time between now and then; if such a thing is physically possible, I shall do it. However, that's unlikely."

The transaction is crossed because Frank was in the critical parent and thus expected John to come back in a child ego state, rather than the adult, which he chose instead.

John can restart the transaction by again insisting on the adult ego state. If Frank comes back with an adult statement, John has succeeded. If Frank is going to start the transaction again, nothing prohibits him from using the critical parent again. If he does, though, that transaction will also likely be crossed. Both sides could try to initiate transactions, but until they stop being crossed, each will end. Of course, use of the third move is possible; see the next question.

6   What is a third move? Explain how an employee could make a third move work when talking with an angry or frustrated boss.

A third move is an attempt to continue the transaction once it has become crossed. This tactic often begins a new transaction that will turn out to be complementary. The trick in the third move is not to let yourself get

hooked into the kind of transaction the other person wants to pull you into:

Employee (calm, businesslike tone): I need some feedback on the DuMont marketing plan.

Boss (harsh, critical tone): This marketing plan for DuMont is the stupidest thing I've ever seen! What were you thinking about?

Employee (calm, businesslike tone): Please show me the areas in the plan that need to be changed.

7   Why is the concept of stroking important in business situations? What does negative stroking involve? Who needs stroking? How can stroking help relationships with customers? With employees?

Positive strokes can be beneficial to the workplace in several ways; a positive stroke is anything one person does to recognize the accomplishments and worth of another. Negative stroking, of course, can involve gameplaying.

Everyone needs strokes, including employees, managers, and customers. The trick is to learn to sense the comfort zone for stroking, which everyone has in different levels. Be sure not to overstroke or understroke. Notice the similarities between the concepts of stroking and positive reinforcement (Chapter 6).

In the workplace, managers "get what they stroke." If you stroke tardiness, you'll get late employees. If you stroke high productivity, you'll get efficient employees.

8   What specific steps can you take when you suspect you are dealing with a game player? What steps can you take to prevent yourself from initiating games?

The adult ego state is the most trustworthy weapon in such a case. Try to stay in the adult whenever you even suspect a game is being attempted. The best way to stop a game is to refuse to play. You can also:

- Work on improving your own self-esteem. Low self-esteem is the most important reason why people play games.
- Get the other person's adult ego state "hooked." Try to lead the would-be gameplayer into using his or her adult ego state.
- Use positive stroking as a preventative measure. Much gameplaying is based on negatives. Getting rid of those negatives is a good method of also getting rid of games.
- De-emphasize the weaknesses of others. Everyone has both weaknesses and strengths. Which do you tend to emphasize when evaluating others?

Critical Thinking Questions

9 How can a knowledge of transactional analysis improve human relations in business situations? How can it help you recognize a game before you become hooked into playing it?

It seems that the most practical value in TA application is being able to see what has happened to a transaction after the fact, and then to work on improving transactions with the same person in the future. Quite often, the average human does not think fast enough to apply transactional analysis to every individual transaction as it is happening—at least at first. TA can increase your overall awareness of the kinds of negative and time-wasting interactions that are taking place in the workplace. Point out to students that several other areas of this textbook deal with areas that can also be dealt with using TA ("Creativity and Human Relations," Chapter 12; "Conflict Management," Chapter 13; "Winning and Keeping Your Customers," Chapter 15).

The way to recognize a game is to watch for repetitive statements and behaviors in yourself and others. Sometimes the payoff is obvious (with "Now I've Got You," for example), and you can immediately tell that a game has been played. Once you have identified the game, identify the payoff. What is the game player expecting to get as a payoff from playing it? To answer the last part of this question honestly, one often cannot avoid the first game someone plays.

10 Think of a conflict situation you were in recently. Define the terms assertiveness and aggressiveness. Then answer these questions: a) What role did aggressiveness or assertiveness play in the conflict? b) Were you aggressive, assertive, or passive? c) Did the situation work out the way you expected? d) Would you act differently if you had to do it again?

This very open-ended question will be answered differently by each student. The main beginning point is to be sure they understand the terms aggressiveness and assertiveness as they are defined in the book:

Assertiveness: Standing up for your own rights without attempting to threaten the self-esteem of others.

Aggressiveness: Going too far in standing up for your personal rights, to the point of hurting others and putting them on the defensive.

If students state that they reacted aggressively or passively, ask them how the situation led them to take that role. Did it work best for the situation at that time, and would they act differently if they had to do it again?

Working It Out

10.1 New Ways to Respond

Note to instructor: Notice that TA exercises are nearly always arguable, mostly because the English language allows for so many differences in emotional meaning, depending on even small changes in tone of voice. Your students will not be unanimous in their interpretations of these exercises, whether they are discussed or written out. If they are assigned in writing, tell the students ahead of time to write a couple of sentences justifying their interpretation. It is important that they are thinking about and understanding basic TA concepts.

All of the following adult responses are assumed to be spoken in a calm, businesslike manner:

Boss: "What's the matter, can't you ever do anything right?"

Suggested responses: "Give me 10 minutes, and I can locate the error and straighten it out for you."

"I'll have the info for you as soon as I can establish what the order number was. Can you give me a minute?"

Customer: "Is there anyone in your company who has one living brain cell?"

Suggested responses: (Quite honestly, a bit of sympathetic parent might be useful here, followed by an adult response.) "I really am sorry that you've had such a runaround. Now, let's get this data down completely and correctly so we can be sure that this will be your last stop here today."

"Maybe not, Mr. Smith, but I, for one, am determined to get to find out what happened to your policy."

Husband: "Why do you always have to be running off to work functions and church activities? Did it ever occur to you that you have a family to care for?"

Suggested responses: "Let's sit down and discuss *both* of our family responsibilities. We do need to understand each other better."

"Maybe I have been spending too much time away from the family; let's talk about it."

Customer: "I got this part for my washing machine here yesterday and it doesn't fit. I've about had it with your incompetence. Give me my money back and make it snappy."

Suggested responses: "I would like to double-check this part if you'd let me. I think we have the one you need. It will take only a minute or two."

"Here's your money. I hope you'll come back again and let us prove to you that we're not incompetent."

Employee: "Gee, I can't seem to figure out how to get this new computer program to work. I've never been too good with electronic stuff. Will you help me? I'm really frustrated."

Suggested responses: "Give me 10 minutes to finish this errand I'm running. I'll be back then and be able to give your problem my full attention."

"Malcolm Fox in engineering knows spreadsheets really well. I'll ask him if he has time this morning to give you a hand."

Working It Out

10.2 Analyzing Transactions

Diagram and label the following transactions:

1. Manager (calm tone of voice): "Please get these reports out by the end of the day."

Employee (whining tone of voice): "Why are you always criticizing me? What's the matter—don't I always get my reports done on time?"

This is a crossed transaction. The manager is speaking adult to adult. The employee is speaking from adapted child to parent.

2. Employee (pleading tone of voice): "My schedule is really tight. Could you give me a hand with this mass mailing?"

Manager (soothing, calm tone of voice): "Sure, I'll get Jean to help you. Looks like you've got a big job there, all right."

This is a complementary transaction. The employee is in the child (adapted child if you assume a rather whining tone of voice). The manager is coming back with the sympathetic parent that the employee was expecting.

3. Employee: "My schedule is really tight. Could you give me a hand with this mass mailing?" (Meaning: "I don't have the confidence to do this by myself.")

Manager: "Sure, I'll get Jean to help you. Looks like you've got a big job here, all right." (Meaning: "I can never depend on you to finish a job by yourself; you're hopeless.")

This is an ulterior transaction. The surface meaning, which is the same as in transaction #2, is what is said openly—but the deeper and more authentic feelings are the ones in parentheses. The employee is coming from the adapted child, as in one interpretation of #2; the manager, though, does an ulterior transaction which shows him to be coming from the critical parent ego state, rather than the sympathetic parent ego state that he pretends to have.

4. Customer: "I've been standing at this counter for 20 minutes, and you've waited on four people who came in after I did! What gives with you guys? Are you all blind and deaf, or just rude?"

Sales clerk: Look lady, you can yell at somebody else. I'm doing the best I can. If you don't like it, get lost!"

This is a crossed transaction. Assuming that you ascribe strident, authoritarian tones to both, they are in a parent–child/parent–child crossed transaction. Both are playing the part of critical parents to the child of the other. The transaction will not continue.

5. Customer: "I've been standing at this counter for 20 minutes, and you've waited on four people who came in after I did! What gives with you guys? Are you all blind and deaf, or just rude?"

Sales clerk: "I'm very sorry, madam. Sometimes it just gets crazy around here. Now, tell me what you need so we can take care of you quickly; heaven knows, you've been waiting long enough."

This is a complementary transaction, though it's a bit subjective in interpretation. The customer is in the adapted child and is aiming at the clerk's parent. She hooks the sympathetic parent, who—aimed back at her child— calms her down, allowing the transaction to have a chance to continue.

■ INTERNET EXERCISES

Tips for Teachers

1. **Read and Write** Ask students to compare the ideas of Eric Berne with those of the other human relations pioneers discussed in this text. Overall, whose ideas have interested them the most so far: Berne? Deming? Maslow?

2. **Compare and Contrast** Ask students to turn this essay into a definite action plan to cover a short period in the immediate future (e.g., the next two weeks). Offer them extra credit for turning in a summary at the end of that time, in which they evaluate how successful they were at using TA in their daily lives.

10.1 Missing the Glory at Morning Glory

1. Could Karen have kept this situation from ending the way it ended?

Some students will think that Karen could have changed the older woman's behavior by pointing out its negativity. However, when one examines what Karen has done, that possibility doesn't seem very likely. Karen has been forcing the adult, and sometimes likely going into the natural child simply as a coping strategy. If the argument that Karen could have changed Marie's behavior works at all, it would be in the context of her adult reactions being aimed at changing Marie's behavior, rather than with just coping, as they have been.

Others might say that Karen's mistake was not letting Marie know what was and was not acceptable behavior from the very beginning. The counter-argument is that, given Marie's leadership style (see Chapter 8), she would have fired Karen outright should she have tried to set the parameters in that way.

2. What kind of transactions were apparently taking place between Marie and Karen? Be specific. What should Karen have done to prevent this type of transaction from taking place?

Marie was nearly always in the critical parent, and Karen was either in the natural child or the adult. As mentioned in the answer to #1 above, Marie's leadership style made any other action on Karen's part difficult. If Karen had at a certain point decided that she was willing to risk her job in order to effect a change in Marie's behavior, then progress might have taken place. It is that risk-taking element that is often crucial.

3. Diagram the transaction in this case. Now diagram the ideal solution.

The students should first diagram a complementary transaction, with Marie coming from the critical parent, aiming at Karen's child. Then Karen would be coming from the natural child to Marie's parent. The second possibility would be a crossed transaction with Marie coming from the critical parent, aiming at Karen's child, but this time, Karen comes from her own adult and aims at Marie's adult. The ideal solution would be adult–adult complementary.

4. What would you have done in Karen Hartley's place? Why?

This question mostly serves to personalize the preceding three questions. The question will likely stimulate discussion about real life experiences wherein students have actually worked for someone like Marie. Answers will vary widely in a typical class.

Case Study

10.2 The Unproductive Meeting

1. Walter Langley is playing a repetitive game here. What is it called, and what are its payoffs?

It is called "Why don't you?... Yes, but..." Whatever anyone suggests, it just won't work; Walter is sure to find a hitch somewhere. The payoffs are sometimes complex; here are some possible ones:

1) Langley can end the session by reminding his people how well educated and intelligent they all are. Then, the implication is that even these bright and capable people can't come up with a solution, I don't feel or look so bad, because I don't have a good solution either. The payoff is to look better and feel off the hook, because he has made the situation look truly impossible.

2) Langley can be listening carefully until he finds a truly exciting solution. Then he can change it just a bit, then call another meeting in a few days to announce "his" new proposal for turning the company around. The payoff is to look like the brains behind the company.

3) (This one could overlap with either of the other two.) By showing how wrong all of the others' ideas are, Langley can look like the real expert. He can discern problems the others didn't see.

2. What can Langley's team do to end this game? Be specific.

They could tell him that they have been attending these meetings for some time with no real results. Then someone on the team should ask him for his suggestion as to how the company can be turned around. Game terminated.

Whatever the students come up with, it should include a refusal to play the game. Indeed, that element will be the answer to the second part of the question. It takes two sides to play a game; when one side refuses, the game is over.

3. Specifically, what would you do if you were in one of Langley's time-wasting meetings?

Answers will vary. Again, student answers should include some method of refusal to continue the game.

Individual and Organizational Change

Chapter 11

LECTURE OUTLINE

I. **Change as a Fact of Life.** Change is something everyone lives with. In the 21st century, the pace of change has picked up greatly.
   A. People are now learning to emphasize the quality factor in change.
   B. Important changes happen to everyone, and intense change is a part of being human.

II. **The Seven Major Life Changes.** Severe change can create tremendous stress. The **Holmes–Rahe Readjustment Scale** rates intensity of types of change.
   A. Usually this type of change involves something coming to an end, but these events are not always negative. The most important dramatic changes can be placed in seven categories:
      1. Loss
      2. Separation
      3. Relocation
      4. A change in relationship
      5. A change in direction
      6. A change in health
      7. Personal growth
   B. These **seven major life changes** have basic characteristics in common:
      1. They happen to everyone.
      2. Most of them seem to happen uncontrollably.
      3. Each one of these changes has its own "babies," or related changes.
      4. The results of change are felt before, during, and after the event.

III. **The Seven Stages of Personal Change**
   A. People need to go through each of the **seven stages of personal change** in order to recover completely.
      1. Emotional Standstill. The reality of the event produces a different mental state, no matter how much advance notice you have.
      2. Denial. Although many people will accept in their minds what has happened, they will continue to deny it with their emotions.

3. Anger. Some form of anger usually follows the denial stage.
4. Helplessness. This step is also called "trying but still failing."
5. Bottoming out. At this point, you are allowing the life-completing processes to take their course.
6. Experimenting. At this point, your normal curiosities and desires to experiment are coming back to life.
7. Completion. The cycle is complete even though **regression** may occur by which the past may re-emerge. The event has become a part of your active memory, a part that you can think about without undue pain.
   B. Shad Helmstetter's Six Steps for Dealing With Change can be used for any kind of change.
      1. Recognize and understand the change.
      2. Make the decision whether to accept or reject the change.
      3. Choose the attitude you are going to have toward the change.
      4. Choose the style that you are going to use to deal with the change. Will you retreat, actively resist, attack, actively accept, or partner?
      5. Choose the action that you are going to take every day.
      6. Review the steps and evaluate your progress daily.

IV. **Models of Organizational Change.** These are changes in the organization that a group of people must be convinced to accept, then taught how to implement:
   A. A change model outlines the steps one must take to change an organization effectively. First, the *individuals* who work for a company have to be convinced that a change is essential. Second, the *systems* of an organization need to be changed. Third, the *organizational climate* must be changed.

B. The **Lewin change model** contains three steps: unfreezing the status quo, moving to a new condition, and refreezing to create a new status quo.
  1. Unfreezing. On the individual level, the unfreezing could involve promoting employees, letting them go, or preparing them for the change. On the structural level, redesigning an entire organization could be the focus of the change effort. On the climate level, the company evaluates how employees are reacting to the proposed changes.
  2. Moving to another condition. This is the step where the actual changes are made. On the individual level, people are developing new skills required for the change. On the structural level, people see changes in actual organizational relationships. On the climate level, they see more openness and trust and fewer conflicts.
  3. Refreezing. The refreezing might involve new hiring policies so that employees hired after the change would be more accepting of the new order.
  4. Current criticisms of the Lewin change model:
     a. Since the mid-1990s the Lewin model has been criticized for applying only to stable times, not to the whitewater rapids business climate of the past decade or so.
     b. This model is still useful if one carefully scrutinizes the refreezing step.
C. **Force field analysis** is a change model that sees the status quo as a battlefield being fought for by two armed forces: one trying to take it over for change, and the others, the restraining forces, trying to defend it.
D. **Logical incrementalism** is a model that acknowledges that bringing about changes in a large organization is usually time-consuming and complicated. The five stages of logical incrementalism are:
  1. General concern. A vague feeling or awareness of a threat or opportunity.
  2. Broadcasting a general concern or idea without details.
  3. Development of a formal plan for change.
  4. The use of an opportunity or a crisis to urge the use of the change plan.
  5. Ongoing adaptation of the plan.
V. **Why Employees Resist Change**
  A. Hearing only what they want to hear.
  B. Fear of the unknown.
  C. Fear of loss.
  D. Resentment of the **change agent**.
  E. Belief that the change is the wrong one.
  F. Rebellion against the speed of the change.

VI. **The Japanese Approach** to change management shows a remarkable adaptability to change. Employees are involved in change decisions, and managers communicate change well. Here are some procedures they follow:
  A. Japanese managers involve employees with the change process from the beginning.
  B. Before a change takes place, Japanese managers spend hours studying the problem.
  C. Japanese companies have fewer layers of management, which reduces red tape and bureaucracy and encourages communication.
  D. If a problem comes up, Japanese companies don't blame employees; they blame the process, system, or management.
VII. **Organizational Development** is a company-wide, planned, systematic method of change achievement in an organization. An **OD change agent**, or outside consultant, may assist using **OD interventions** or training tools. Today OD is often used for **empowerment**. It requires the participation and support of top management. The main factors are:
  A. Participative operations. The more employees are involved with a change effort, the better.
  B. Equality. De-emphasize hierarchy and heavy-handed authority.
  C. Respect for others. People should be treated with respect and fairness.
  D Confrontation. Problems are to be confronted and dealt with immediately.
  E. Trust and mutual support. Openness and trust are productive in any organization.

11.1 Managing Personal Change in the Workplace
  1. Become aware of it.
  2. Talk about the change.
  3. Maintain the organizational ideal. You are not doing anyone a favor by allowing the workplace to be a temporary vacation spot.

11.2 Breaking Down the Resistance to Change in Your Organization. Resistance to change is often caused by poor communication, which results in a hazy understanding of the purpose and consequences of the change.
  1. Create a climate in which change is acceptable. The manager's responsibility is to create a work environment that allows employees to be comfortable with change.
  2. Involve everyone in the change effort. People who have been involved with the creation of a change will find it very difficult to resist that change.

ANSWERS TO IN-CHAPTER QUESTIONS

PHOTO, page 329: Does Geri appear to be responding to her major life changes in a positive way? What are some signs that help you form your answer? Would you respond the same way?

Yes. She makes the decision to accept the changes, take on the new challenges, and make the necessary adjustments. Students' answers will vary.

FIGURE 11.1, page 332: When you think about it, how serious were these changes to you?

Think hard before answering this because you may tend to downplay the difficulties of changes that are behind you. Your answer will depend on the types of changes you have experienced, as well as how you reacted to them.

FIGURE 11.2, page 334: How can you ensure that you moved through each stage with awareness and ease?

Just by being aware of these stages, you can educate yourself as to what is happening to you emotionally during a major life change. With this knowledge, you can anticipate the change process and know how to respond to it.

PHOTO, page 335: When have you felt yourself dealing with a problem through denial?

Unfortunately, almost any situation can be avoided through denial. One example of denial is when students know their grades are not as high as they should be, but avoid solving the problem by telling themselves that their grades will improve on their own.

FIGURE 11.3, page 338: How does this six-step list help you adjust to any change?

It teaches that all changes should be acknowledged and understood in the ways shown. It will also help you make clearer and more thoughtful decisions about whether you accept or like a change—as well as how to make progress through that change.

PHOTO, page 339: How tolerant toward change are you, and do you think you could increase your tolerance?

Your tolerance level depends on your personality and also on your individual work situation. You should increase your risk tolerance only to the extent to which you feel comfortable, and to which it will not endanger your career and security.

FIGURE 11.4, page 341: What is the chief criticism of the Lewin change model?

Some criticize it because of the final step, refreezing. In today's hectic business environment, refreezing to a past way of doing things may not be possible or even desirable. Despite this, the first two steps of this change model are still helpful.

FIGURE 11.5, page 343: What are the positive effects of this change model?

Force field analysis encourages planning, allows the pro-change forces to analyze their opponents, and can possibly avoid conflict by this careful analysis.

PHOTO, page 345: How have you seen change resisted in an organization, and what happened?

People resist change in many ways, from leaving the company to simply slowing down their work efforts due to lowered morale. Communicating with employees and making them feel like part of the change process will help dispel fears and encourage successful change.

FIGURE 11.6, page 348: What can you do when you encounter resistance to change?

Communicate with the other person and find out what they are scared of, then demonstrate to them how the change will benefit the organization and themselves.

FIGURE 11.7, page 349: How is the Japanese approach different from approaches you have witnessed?

Answers will vary, but many American employees have not seen the same level of analysis and communication that Japanese employees do. In addition, the blame factor that is so often seen in American companies is discouraged in Japan, since it does more to create problems than solve them.

PHOTO, page 349: Could your current organization (or the one for which you worked most recently) benefit from this approach?

Regardless of the circumstances, the answer is yes.

PHOTO, page 351: How can talking to an employee maintain the organizational ideal?

Talking to an employee prevents misunderstandings and allows the employee to voice his or her feelings about the situation. It also allows for the employer to understand the employee's situation and set goals around those new limitations.

Review Questions

1 **Many major changes are listed in the Holmes–Rahe Readjustment Scale. What characteristics do they all have in common? Explain. What factors would you add to or otherwise change in this scale?**

They all represent parts of people's lives that change their reality dramatically. No blanket judgment of good or bad can be placed on these events, because they include happy events (such as marriage and holidays), as well as extremely negative ones. Also, all of these events represent something that had become a norm that is now ending. The ending is what causes the readjustment problems.

In addition, the answers that correspond to the text are as follows:

1. These changes happen to everyone at some time in their lives.
2. Most of these changes seem to happen uncontrollably.
3. Each of these changes has its own "babies," or offspring changes that affect other parts of people's lives.
4. People feel the results of these changes before, during, and after the event.

2 **Explain the seven steps of personal change management. Why are they all essential?**

These seven steps need to be taken by anyone who is going through a deep personal change. In other words, these steps represent the process of healthy reaction to such change. Because this is a normal progression, skipping one step will usually mean that the person who has skipped it will have to return at a later time and go through the missed step or its equivalent.

1. Emotional Standstill. The first step is shock—shock so overwhelming that it does away with other emotions for a period of time. Even when the event is expected, an element of shock still exists. No matter how much advance notice you may have, the reality of the event produces a different mental state for a while.
2. Denial. Although many people accept in their minds what has happened, they will continue to deny it emotionally. Ideally, this denial period will be over in a few weeks or months.
3. Anger. Some form of anger usually follows the denial stage. This anger must be dealt with, not denied.
4. Helplessness. The person undergoing the change is still suffering from the ending that has taken place. Here, the suffering person is afraid to bottom out because despair is a helpless condition, and most people don't want to feel helpless. Thus, people in this stage will usually make one of two mistakes: Either they will try to share their emotions with too many other people, or they will retreat into isolation.
5. Bottoming out. Bottoming out means releasing the thoughts, tensions, memories, and emotions that force you to hold onto the past. Though sometimes dramatic, this step is usually arrived at gradually. Finally, the suffering person can let go of the emotional burden, and the life-completing processes are being allowed to take their course.
6. Experimenting. In this stage, normal curiosities and desires to experiment begin to reemerge. The sufferer is now emotionally available for other people and other projects.
7. Completion. The cycle is now complete. The sufferer might still be haunted by the past, and on some days he or she will feel that no progress has been made from the second or third step. This occasional regression is normal. In general, though, the traumatic event has become a part of the active memory, a part that one can recall without undue pain.

3 **Pretend you are a manager with an employee who is going through a painful divorce that is affecting his or her quality of job performance. How could the material in this chapter be helpful to you?**

If you ever experienced a similar trauma, you might be more likely to be able to empathize. Even if common experiences are shared, though, you may not always understand the sufferer because everyone goes through the seven steps at different speeds and with varying intensities. A study of the seven-step process allows another person to identify the normal reactions most people have to traumatic change.

Managers should not allow themselves to yield to the temptation of becoming a psychological counselor to employees. There is a safe distance between understanding and helping an employee and becoming a counselor. (Chapter 18 deals with appropriate procedures for managers in such instances.)

4 **Do you agree with the critics of the Lewin change model who say that it is no longer relevant—especially refreezing? Why or why not?**

Whatever students answer to this question, they should at least understand the model. They cannot disagree with a principle intelligently unless they understand it. Below is a longer version of what students have read in the text; you can share it with them, especially if they have trouble understanding the basic model.

1. Recognizing the need for change. This is necessary is the first step. If you are an employee or supervisor who can see a need that nobody else seems to discern, you need to do some selling.

2. Identifying the best change method. There are numerous change methods available to any organization. Some specific techniques involve survey feedback and team building (see Chapter 9). The technique that a firm chooses should meet its needs in reacting to the need for change.

3. Unfreezing. This is the first step in the basic three-part model. If people in the workplace are going to change their attitudes, their current attitudes and beliefs need to be altered—or unfrozen, as Lewin calls it. Unfreezing is removing resistance to change. This can be done by building trust and confidence, developing open communication, and encouraging employee participation. Though the unfreezing process often foments self-doubt in individuals, it also provides a means of overcoming it. Most importantly, if members of an organization are to be receptive to change, they must be made to feel they can and should change.

4. Moving to a new condition is the second step in the basic three-part model. The actual changes are made at this point. It is important in this step to develop a two-way relationship between the people attempting to implement the change and those who are being asked to change. As mentioned in the text, the new condition might involve either structural or climatic changes.

5. Refreezing. This is the third step in the basic three-part model. In this stage, the organization ensures that the new attitudes, beliefs, and behaviors will actually become the new norms—the new status quo—on the job. If employees change to a new set of attitudes and work habits for two weeks, then revert to the way things were, the change has not been complete.

⑤ Briefly explain how force field analysis can be helpful to someone attempting change in an organization.

Force field analysis, also developed by Lewin, has been called a battlefield model. The status quo is seen as a battlefield, with driving forces on one side and restraining forces on the other. If nothing else, this model helps one become more articulate about exactly what is happening in the change process, what the balances of power on each side mean, and what forces need to be broken down for a successful change effort to take place. As the text points out, the task is to build up the driving forces and weaken the restraining forces in order to win.

Anyone attempting to change an organization can be helped by using this model to identify the forces on each side, including an analysis of which opposing elements are the most vulnerable and which driving forces are the strongest. In short, the model helps you identify the playing pieces on your gameboard.

⑥ Someone once said that recognizing the need for change is the most difficult step in the change process. Why would that be true? Explain.

Imagine a business in the early 1980s, plugging along with managers who were unaware that a computer revolution was about to happen. Somewhere, management needed to receive the information that showed them how very important computerizing their business was going to be in the near future. Actually, many businesses continued to attempt to operate without computers during that period of history until they finally were overtaken by their competition and went bankrupt. Others finally saw the need for change, but the vision came too late and they either went out of business or lost a substantial market share.

This situation illustrates just how hard it is sometimes to see the need for change. So many emotional elements are involved, including fear of the unknown, fear of having one's own ignorance exposed, and comfort with the status quo. In other words, people often rationally know that a change is necessary, but emotional reasons prevent that knowledge from being transferred into the vision of a need for change. When you are one of the few people in a company who is pushing for a change that seems obviously needed, you can experience tremendous frustration with people who refuse to see that need.

⑦ Explain the concepts behind logical incrementalism. Make sure to discuss the different steps that organizations go through based on James Brian Quinn's research of meaningful changes within organizations. Do you find this model helpful? Why or why not? Do you think it would ever be helpful in managing change in a smaller company? Why or why not?

Logical incrementalism addresses the complexity of the change processes, especially in large organizations. James Brian Quinn based this model on research of actual organizations that were involved in meaningful changes. The steps that most organizations go through are:

1. General concern. This is similar to "recognizing the need for change" at the beginning of the Lewin change model, but here the need for

change is vague. It may be a threat from competition or some other force, or the perception of a great opportunity about to be missed, that starts the process.

2. Broadcasting a general concern or idea without details. For example, a CEO tells his middle managers, "This company has to be restructured; it simply contains too many levels of management." Just what the new structuring would entail is not mentioned, because at this point it has not been thought out.

3. Developing a formal plan for change. Restructuring can be used as a continuing example. At this point, a new tentative organizational chart would be developed and, at length, unveiled.

4. The use of an opportunity or a crisis to urge change. "If we don't implement this new restructuring, jobs (or hours) will be lost," would be an effective line here.

5. Ongoing adaptation of the plan. Unlike the refreezing step in the Lewin change model, this last step emphasizes the numerous ongoing readjustments that are necessary when any new plan is implemented in a larger company.

To the last part of the question, student responses will vary. Often, students who have worked for a large organization will value this model more than others will. You might also point out to students that this model is descriptive, rather than simply prescriptive. That is, it is based on a description of the steps that actually take place in larger companies that are changing—steps that seem to have worked in most cases.

Whether it would be valuable to a small company is an open question, although it has been used in small companies with some success.

8 What is organizational development? How is it used in a company that wants change? On what types of change does it usually focus?

Organizational development (OD) is a planned and systematic attempt to change an organization. The change agent is either an outside consultant or consultant group that specializes in such change efforts, or someone inside the company who is trained as an OD consultant. Typically, the changes in OD are aimed at humanizing the environment, which of course makes OD extremely relevant to a study of human relations.

Critical Thinking Questions

9 How has change impacted your own life? When you reflect on your past, which changes were positive? Which changes were negative? Did changes that you originally thought would be negative, turn out to be positive? In general, do you see change as mostly a positive or negative force? Explain why.

Answers will vary. Some changes are undeniably negative, but many will have some positive effects. For instance, a divorce may lead to a relocation to a new city that the person enjoys more than the last. Ask students if they believe that most changes have positive and negative elements.

10 Identify organizations you have seen or heard about that resisted change. Why did they resist change? What consequences did such companies suffer, if any?

Answers will vary. Today's examples often have to do with delays in building company Web sites and creating an online presence. These delays can result in lost sales and market share, being unable to secure a good domain name, or throwing together a poorly-constructed Web site in a small amount of time.

■ INTERNET EXERCISES

Tips for Teachers

1. **Read and Write** Ask students to consider situations in which the Lewin change model is still completely applicable. Since not all businesses are fast-paced or experience rapid change, does this change model still work in many areas? Also, could it work better in cultures with less time urgency than the U.S.?

2. **Self-Assessment** This is a good time to ask students to also consider the importance of voluntary change in their lives. Apart from their tolerance of change, how much do they actually like it? Some will report changing jobs fairly often, moving to different areas, and doing everything they can to avoid settling down; others will admit to a dislike of unnecessary change. Then ask them to compare their desire for change to their tolerance of it. How closely related are the two? Does a general acceptance of change help when unwanted and negative change (such as a death in the family) occurs?

Working It Out

11.1 Turbulent World Tolerance Test

This short test can be effective as an in class exercise. It can be especially useful to discuss the test results with students after they have finished. Many of the issues that come up in such a discussion will be directly related to subjects in the chapter.

Case Study

11.1 The Web Page Fiasco

1. Do you agree that fear is likely the main issue here? If not, what other factors might be involved?

Fear is, indeed, the likeliest cause. However, fear of what? Students will likely mention:

- Fear of the unknown. These two managers have apparently never worked on the receiving end of a Web page. They don't know the intricacies of the process, and that gives them a certain kind of fear.
- Fear of loss of control. If they do get a Web site, who (if anyone) will really be controlling and maintaining it? Perhaps someone else they don't like or trust will actually be running things.
- Fear of other types of loss. This could include simply the loss of the status quo. After all, the way things work now are predictable and understandable. Why lose that order and predictability? Ultimately, the greatest fear is of losing one's position in the company.
- Fear of being exposed. When this type of high technology comes into a company, people might start to see them as less capable and less "on top of things," since high tech is not their chief competence.

Students might think of other types of fears.

Another factor that might be mentioned is ignorance. These two simply don't know as much as they should, nor as much as they could if they would only spend a little time learning. Also, perhaps Doug and Marge simply don't know the first step; they don't know where to begin. Another possibility is procrastination. Students will likely think of several more.

2. Assume for a moment that fear is at least a major issue here. What can Carole and Eldon do, as marketing specialists, to attack the fear that seems to be delaying progress to a danger point?

Since the company is quite small, they might have more impact than they would in a larger organization. They can talk to Doug and Marge candidly with suggestions as to how to help. They can find a Web designer who will approach them to show how simple and relatively inexpensive creating a Web page can be. Most importantly, they need to do something, if for no other reason than the fact that they acutely see the need. In the 21st century, a Web page is becoming increasingly essential to success for nearly any business.

3. Briefly evaluate the client council conference as a device for change suggestions from major clients. Would such an approach work in other types of organizations?

The client council conference as described in the case is an effective avenue for communication between larger customers and the company. It is also a method of thanking regular customers for the parts they have played in the firm's success. The period where a consultant comes in and receives negative input without company personnel being present is an excellent way to find out what changes really need to be made. You might want to ask students whether they have ever encountered this concept in a company they have dealt with. If not, explain it fully; then get student input on pros and cons. Two disadvantages are expense and time consumption. Do the advantages outweigh the disadvantages?

Case Study

11.2 ■ The Family Tragedy

1. How could an understanding of the Seven Steps of Personal Change help everyone at Javca?

A knowledge of the personal change process is helpful because it aids in understanding the normal mending process. Students should be taught that this process is normal and healthy. In fact, the only truly unhealthy action in personal change is not following this progression. Skipping steps is especially detrimental, for one is usually doomed to returning to the missed step sometime later. Temporary loss of self-esteem is often a by-product of loss. Knowledge of these steps can help the suffering individual understand that such reactions are normal and to be expected—but temporary.

2. Explain the grief counselor's statement, "It sounds like everybody at Javca needs this, not just Juanita."

The employees at Javca need a knowledge of the steps for at least two reasons. First, the knowledge will help them understand the change process of their coworker, Juanita. When she is expressing anger, for example, they can understand that anger is one of the early steps in the process. Second, although their grief is certainly less intense than Juanita's, many of them are going through a similar series of steps with this loss.

3. There are some obvious disadvantages to the company in keeping Juanita at work at this time. What are some advantages of having her remain on the job during her healing process?

Some individuals are not as strong as Juanita seems to be, so perhaps an extended time off will be necessary for some people in this situation. However, if staying on the job is what Juanita prefers to do, there are advantages to both the company and the employee in allowing her to remain. The first one is obvious: financial reasons. Juanita is now living on one income; as the head of her household, she has an added burden to stay afloat financially, so staying away from work is not going to help her feel more secure in that area. Also, simply staying busy is often a crucial medicine in the healing process. If Juanita wants to stay working and can remain focused enough to do her work, the work itself and the support from her coworkers can both be helpful. This is especially true in a case like this, where the employees knew and appreciated her partner.

Creativity and Human Relations

LECTURE OUTLINE

I. **The Creativity Connection.** Competition in the global marketplace is forcing American companies to become more creative.

II. **What Is Creativity?**
   A. Creativity is not related to personality type, creative media, products, or environment.
   B. **Creativity** is the ability to produce ideas or solutions that are original and useful.
   C. Csikszentmihalyi says creative people have flexible and fluent ideas, and know good ideas from bad.
   D. **Intuition** is direct perception or insight.

III. **Perception and Creativity**
   A. Creativity is often blocked by uncreative habits in thinking, or **collective habits of thought**.
   B. **Perception** is the way in which you view the world, and viewing the world in a different way from your usual way opens up creativity.
   C. Creative people have characteristics in common: expert knowledge, openness to new experiences, independent spirit, internal motivation, and persistence.
      1. Internal (**intrinsic**) **motivators** motivate a person from within.
      2. Extrinsic (**external**) **motivators** motivate by outside forces.

IV. **Creativity and Intelligence—or Creative Intelligence**
   A. Creativity requires **intuition** more than academic **intelligence** or scholastic ability.
   B. Being a genius does not guarantee creativity, but most creative people have average or above-average intelligence.
   C. Gardner's theory of **eight intelligences** challenges the notions of traditional intelligence, and comes closer to this book's conceptions of creativity. These areas of intelligence include: language intelligence, math and logic intelligence, musical intelligence, spatial reasoning intelligence, movement (kinesthetic) intelligence, interpersonal intelligence, intrapersonal intelligence, and naturalist intelligence.

V. **Creativity in the Workplace**
   A. Many employers and managers discourage creativity in employees; top administrators think of ideas.
   B. Employers should encourage creativity.
   C. Corporate creativity can be encouraged.

VI. **Creative Methods for Groups**
   A. **Brainstorming** involves holding sessions with a relaxed atmosphere for employees to come up with creative ideas together.
   B. The **nominal group method** is a structured activity that includes coming up with creative ideas in a group, writing them down, allowing everyone to read them, then vote.

 12.1 The Creative Process: Hatching a New Idea
   1. Preparation
   2. Incubation
   3. Illumination
   4. Translation/verification

Strategy for Success 12.2 Increase Your Creativity
   1. Get into the **open mode**.
   2. Think of yourself as a creative person. Increase your **self-perception**.
   3. Learn to see problems as opportunities.
   4. Look for more than one or two solutions to a problem. Avoid the **either/or fallacy**. Look for the **second** (third, fourth, and so on) **right answer**.
   5. Learn to play the violin, or get out of your comfort zone and try new experiences.
   6. Turn your ideas into action.
   7. Don't be afraid to break the rules, especially when they outlive their usefulness and situations change (**Aslan phenomenon**).
   8. Don't be afraid to make mistakes.
   9. Spend time with creative people.
   10. Capture creative ideas when they happen.

ANSWERS TO IN-CHAPTER QUESTIONS

PHOTO, page 365: Do you agree with the employee about Denny's and Jaime's creativity? How could they improve their creative thinking skills?

Student's answers will vary. Denny and Jaime should set a time to discuss ideas with their employees. Denny and Jaime should value everyone's ideas and input, and reach an agreement together about which ideas are best.

PHOTO, page 367: What do you do after illumination?

After the excitement of illumination dies down, you enter the translation/verification stage. This is where you *translate* the idea into action, and *verify* it by making sure that your solution is based on a correct understanding of the facts.

FIGURE 12.1, page 370: In what areas do you want to be more creative?

This answer will vary depending on your personality and how happy you are with it. If you answered "true" to question 1, perhaps you want to start getting in the habit of seeing things from a different perspective, or start looking for more than one "right" answer to problems.

PHOTO, page 372: What inventions would you like to create?

This is a fun question because you can allow yourself to dream, and to realize that you can invent something if you give yourself the time and creative thinking skills to do so. Your answer can be anything—as long as you consider it worthwhile.

FIGURE 12.2, page 374: In what areas of creative intelligence are you strongest?

A quick look at your favorite activities and greatest successes will tell you this. If you have always been an outstanding athlete and writer, then your obvious areas are Language and Movement. However, looking back to the Johari Window in Chapter 3, you may have many other talents and not even realize it.

PHOTO, page 375: How do you define intelligence?

Your answer may include reasoning ability, but should not stop at that alone. Read further about the eight intelligences, then decide if your answer has changed.

FIGURE 12.3, page 378: How can your workplace benefit from increased creativity?

Answers will vary, but many people feel that if employees have more opportunities to speak from experience and offer new ideas, their companies would improve dramatically.

PHOTO, page 385: How does creativity play a role in invention?

An invention cannot be conceived until someone has the creativity to pinpoint the need for it. It cannot be built until a creative mind searches for the right materials and design. Finally, it cannot be completed until the creative mind decides that it has reached its optimum state and needs no further improvement.

CHAPTER REVIEW, pages 392–397

Review Questions

❶ Is creativity the same as intelligence? How are they related? In what ways are they different?

Intelligence and creativity are not the same thing. Creative people are usually intelligent, but many intelligent people are not creative. Creativity requires coming up with new and original ideas to solve problems. Creative people can find several correct answers to a problem, while those who are regarded as intelligent tend to come up with one right answer.

Gardner's eight intelligences come closer to identifying creativity than do the traditional definitions of intelligence. He says that everyone has strengths in different areas, and should capitalize on those strengths.

❷ Consider the eight types of intelligences: verbal, math/logical, musical, spatial, bodily kinesthetic, interpersonal, intrapersonal, and naturalist. Think of a celebrity or other well-known person for each of these categories of intelligence.

Answers will vary, and the list of possibilities is endless! Students should include well-known celebrities or other people who clearly embody the type of intelligence described. Here are a few suggestions:

Verbal: Any author will work here. Some possibilities include William Shakespeare, Geoffrey Chaucer, Charlotte and Emily Brontë, Mark Twain, Langston Hughes, Robert Frost, Zora Neale Hurston, and Toni Morrison.

Math/logical: Albert Einstein is an obvious choice here.

Musical: Any well-known musician is appropriate here. Bach, Beethoven, Mozart, Tchaikovsky, Miles Davis, John Lennon, Ella Fitzgerald, and many more names will come up.

Spatial: Inventors such as the Wright brothers, Leonardo da Vinci, and Thomas Edison would work here. Architects such as Frank Lloyd Wright are appropriate as well, and so are artists known for their understanding of dimension and space, such as Picasso or Michelangelo.

Bodily kinesthetic: Professional athletes, such as Tiger Woods, Michael Jordan, Larry Bird, Florence Griffith Joyner, and others, are often named. Professional dancers, such as Mikhail Barishnikov and Martha Graham, would fit this category as well.

Interpersonal: Famous persons who are known for the accomplishments as mediators or conflict managers are appropriate here. These might include Madeleine Albright, Jimmy Carter, Nelson Mandela, Mother Teresa, Desmond Tutu, and Eleanor Roosevelt.

Intrapersonal skill is a little more difficult to demonstrate, since it is not possible to observe the process of introspection. People whose lives have focused on self-understanding would work here, such as Sigmund Freud, Anna Freud, Carl Jung, or Erik Erikson.

Naturalist intelligence is an understanding of nature and natural processes. Jane Goodall and Dian Fossey come to mind here.

❸ Why do workplaces so often lack creativity? What steps can managers take to increase the quality and quantity of their employees' creative output?

It is often easier for managers and employers to uphold the status quo than to make an effort to set up conditions that encourage creativity. Their motto might be "If it ain't broke, don't fix it." Some employers believe it is more appropriate for new ideas to come from top levels of administration; others simply do not know how to encourage the process. Still more may think new ideas will cost too much to institute, while others (as discussed in earlier chapters) are uncomfortable with any kind of change. What they don't realize is that their reluctance to allow or encourage creativity is resulting in lost productivity and lowered morale among employees.

❹ What does it mean to be in the open mode? What does this feel like? How can the open mode allow for greater creativity?

The **open mode** is an attitude of openness to new ideas, flexibility in thought processes, and thoughtfulness. It is less goal-directed or purposeful, more expansive, and more fun than the closed mode. The open mode is more conducive to new and creative ideas. Because there is less time pressure and everyday worry in the open mode, it is more pleasant and contains less anxiety and more relaxation. All these combined produce a mood and attitude that allow for creativity thoughts to emerge.

❺ Explain the difference between brainstorming and the nominal group method. How can both help produce more creative group results?

Brainstorming is less structured. It requires a relaxed, playful, almost silly atmosphere. People who are brainstorming are encouraged to build on each other's ideas and are not allowed to ridicule ideas, no matter how impractical. In a later session, ideas are discussed in a more rational atmosphere and ranked in order of usefulness. Everyone's input is valued.

The **nominal group method** is more structured and less playful than brainstorming. Group members list ideas separately, and a recorder writes them down on a flip chart or white board (or chalkboard) so that everyone can see them. The group then discusses the merits of the ideas, and decides which to use.

Both help encourage greater creativity because people are asked to share ideas, hear new ideas, and think of new solutions.

❻ How many right answers are there to any one problem? What is meant by the *second right answer*? How many right answers should you look for in solving a problem, before deciding on a solution to implement?

There are probably at least a few (and possibly infinite) correct answers for any one problem. The **second right answer** is an alternative solution to a problem or situation. Take time to think of several right answers before deciding on which solution to implement.

❼ How does the phrase *playing the violin* relate to an increase in creativity? What skill or talent would you like to explore? How would learning a new skill increase your creativity?

Playing the violin means getting out of one's comfort zone and trying a new experience that may be difficult, challenging, or even scary. This can be almost threatening to some people who depend on order and routine and are less creative and more pragmatic.

Students' answers will vary regarding talents they wish to explore.

Learning a new skill in order to increase creativity works because it forces you out of your rut and into a new way of thinking. A nice bonus is that in exploring new ideas, you might become good at the new skill. Success in a new area can then open up a new arena of creative ideas for you.

8 **Which better promotes creativity: positive reinforcement or intrinsic motivation? Explain.**

Both positive reinforcement and intrinsic motivation will successfully increase a desired behavior. Experiments have shown that positive reinforcement can increase both the number of creative projects attempted and the quality of creative work. This positive reinforcement doesn't have to be expensive, complicated, or planned; simple verbal praise works very well. Lack of positive reinforcement in the form of recognition can prevent creativity, and self-esteem is lowered when one's creative ideas are rejected or ridiculed. The end result is lowered self-esteem and morale, and poorer work quality.

Despite all the impact of positive reinforcement, intrinsic motivation is even more powerful. When people are self-fulfilled by the creative work, their creative output is greatly increased. However, extreme extrinsic motivation or reward (positive reinforcement) can crush creativity; people may come to feel that they are working only for the reward, so they convince themselves that they are not really interested in the product itself.

Critical Thinking Questions

9 **Do you think creative geniuses are more likely *born* or *made*? Do you think you could become more creative if you were to work at it?**

Answers will vary, but most students after reading this chapter should say that creativity can be enhanced by practice. In that way, then, creative people are made and not born. But without some natural talent or interest to begin with, even an Einstein (with math-logic skill) cannot be made into an NFL tackle (with kinesthetic ability). Creativity will not appear without an inborn talent. The best answer is that both nature (innate skill) and nurture (environmental influences) work together in making people who they are.

10 **Which type of talent do you think has greater worth to society, creativity or academic intelligence? Why? Do you think one of these is more important than the other?**

Answers will vary. Students may say that American society values academic intelligence over creativity in school as evidenced by the importance placed on getting good grades and doing well on tests. Simultaneously, our culture admires creative artists and musicians, as evidenced by the public adoration and financial profit many of them receive.

INTERNET EXERCISES

Tips for Teachers

1. **Compare and Contrast** Ask students how effective they think creativity tests are, and what (if any) limits they seem to have. Also, ask them if they believe that there are different approaches to creativity; if so, which ones are most helpful to an organization? Which ones would not be as helpful?

2. **Read and Evaluate** Ask students what they learned about their own creativity from performing these exercises and reading these resources. Do any of them feel that understanding and increasing their own creativity was made easier?

Working It Out

12.1 How Creative Are You?

This exercise is a fun way to get the discussion on personal creativity started. Even the hypothetical factor it purports to measure, CQ (or creativity quotient), can spark discussion among students as to its existence.

12.2 Creative Brainstorming

This exercise is designed to stimulate creativity in groups. Students typically have a lot of fun with it. You might want to start this activity by having students brainstorm individually without sharing their ideas at first; then have them do the activity in small groups. In conclusion, have students evaluate whether they are more creative on their own or when working cooperatively.

12.1 Inland's Creative Crunch

1. What creative steps can Garth and Lynn take to turn the tide against the new competition?

Since both Garth and Lynn have admitted that they are fresh out of new ideas, they need to enlist the help of the other store's employees. These 51 employees are probably quite motivated to think of new ideas in order to save their jobs. Employees in accounting, purchasing, and operations probably already have some ideas about improving the situation. Garth and Lynn also need to keep in mind that there may not be one large, all-encompassing solution for everything; several solutions may be necessary to cover different parts of the same problem.

2. How should Garth and Lynn use the talents of their 51 employees?

Garth and Lynn could start by holding group creativity sessions, including brainstorming and the nominal group method, to find out whether their employees can come up with any new ideas. Beyond those two group methods, they can use the corporate creativity suggestions listed in the text in order to spark individual creativity: They can align employees' interests with the organization's goals, allow self-initiated activity among employees, allow time for unofficial activity, encourage serendipity in ideas, provide diverse stimuli, and improve internal company communication. They could even come up with a creative competition among employees to get them to incubate some new ideas.

Other group ideas not mentioned here might work as well. One example of this is the devil's advocate strategy. This strategy forces employees to argue against their own position, while those opposing them must argue in favor of the ideas. This is a good way to see all sides of a potential solution. Another strategy, the fishbowl, forces the person with a creative idea to sit in the middle of a semicircle while answering challenges and questions from the others. Garth and Lynn could also appoint a committee of the most creative employees to think of possible steps in improving their situation.

3. What could Garth have done a year ago to prevent Inland from falling into the position it is in now?

Garth should have started the process of thinking about GroCo's impact as soon as he heard it was coming to his area. He could have received ideas from more people if he had started earlier—especially other small business owners who have been threatened by national chains. By this time, it is probably too late to recruit outside help for thinking of new ideas to save the store. If Garth had started earlier, he would have had much more time to be in the open mode and think of new ideas.

Standard approaches would have included looking at the possibility of better services to customers; a wider product base, and checking out food wholesalers in other parts of the world to see what creative ideas were being tried out—then improving on those trends by creatively adapting them to Inland's selling environment.

12.2 Smarts, Luck, or Skill?

1. Who's right about the definition of creativity: Carlos, Debi, or Susan? Is there more than one right answer to this question?

There is always more than one right answer to any question, as you learned in this chapter! Carlos is partly correct in that creativity requires some kind of intelligence, but he is wrong in thinking that creativity is the same as intelligence. Debi is partly correct in that creativity requires time and luck (such as taking advantage of serendipity when it allows new ideas to emerge), but wrong in thinking that creativity is all due to luck. Susan has the best answer in that creativity can be a skill that is practiced and learned. She can encourage her employees to get into the "open mode," think of themselves as creative people, learn to see problems as opportunities, look for more than one or two solutions to a problem, learn to "play the violin" (get out of their comfort zone and try new experiences), turn their ideas into action, stop being afraid to break the rules, stop being afraid to make mistakes, spend time with creative people, and capture creative ideas as they happen.

2. Suppose you are Susan. What kinds of information would you bring to a meeting on creativity?

Susan should bring the information listed above in question #1 and have her employees discuss this and reflect on it. She should tell them she is committed to creating a corporate culture that supports creativity in employees. She should assure them that creativity does not depend on individual personality, the type of products being made at the business, or other environmental factors; it is not the same as academic success or intelligence. She should tell them they all have skill areas in which they excel (language, math/logical, music, spatial reasoning, movement/kinesthetic, interpersonal, intrapersonal, and naturalistic intelligence) and can learn to capitalize on these strengths. She can also practice group creativity exercises such as brainstorming and the nominal group method with them.

3. Do you see a link between Carlos's creativity slump and his self-esteem? Explain.

Failure at something you value can reduce self-esteem. When self-esteem is low, creativity suffers. This becomes a downward spiral. Therefore, there is a definite link between Carlos's creativity slump and his self-esteem.

■ ADDITIONAL ACTIVITY

Creative Metaphors

Purpose: To encourage creativity by teaching the use of creative metaphors as a form of expression. This exercise is usually fun and can add to creative potential.

Procedure: Use the following examples to encourage participants to create their own metaphors. Divide the class into groups of three to five students and ask each group to use the brainstorming techniques outlined in the text to come up with at least five metaphors they all like. The examples below were actually created by students while the first edition of this text was being written. The instructor can save the best of the metaphors from each group to be used (with permission) in future exercises.

"Life is..." or "Life is like..."

- Life is like a game of Chinese Checkers. If you've lost your marbles, you aren't going to win the game.

- Life is like a rosebud, slowly opening and revealing its vivid hues and rich warm scent. Slowly, its petals fall, though, one by one, enriching the earth and leaving a soft, lingering memory that slowly disappears.

- Life is like reading a long 18th-century novel. By the time you've finished it and figured it out, you've either forgotten the beginning or too much time has gone by for you to care much about any plot—except your burial plot.

- Life is like a tank of gasoline. You start out on full, but move slowly until the reading is half empty. From that point, it takes no time until you run out of fuel, and you still aren't where you planned to be. (This creative metaphor was written by a middle-aged student.)

- Life is like a nudist trying to cross over a barbed-wire fence. Moving carefully and skillfully is the only way to avoid pain. Once you've gotten over the fence, you might have to flee from those people who misunderstand your intentions because they have chosen to judge you by your appearance.

Conflict Management

Chapter 13

LECTURE OUTLINE

I. **Types of Conflict.** Wherever there are people, conflict exists.

   A. **Conflict** is a process that starts when one person damages, or is caught preparing to damage, something that another person cares about. However it is defined, several common aspects are involved:

   1. Conflict must be *perceived* by all people involved in it.

   2. Nearly all definitions of conflict involve opposition or incompatibility.

   3. Some type of interaction has to be involved as well, or all parties would be avoiding conflict.

   B. One way of classifying conflicts is by seeing them as either **functional** or **dysfunctional**—that is, either constructive or destructive. Another way of classifying conflict is by the actors:

   1. **Inner conflict** is conflict within an individual.

   2. **Person versus person conflict** involves two people who are at odds over personality differences, values conflicts, loyalties, or any number of other issues.

   3. **Intragroup conflict** results when two groups form and take sides.

   4. **Person versus group conflict** occurs when a member of a group breaks its norms. It also can involve a nonmember who opposes a group's norms.

II. **Sources of Conflict.** Conflicts start at different points over different issues. If you are aware of the type of conflict you are involved in, that knowledge can help you discover how best to resolve it.

   A. **Content conflict** focuses on disagreements over what a statement or concept means. The issue is whether an idea is right.

   B. **Values conflict** usually goes very deep, but conflicts over values do not occur as often as people usually suspect.

   C. **Negotiation-of-selves conflict** erupts over differences in the self-definition that occurs when people define themselves to others and respond to their implied definitions of themselves.

   D. **Institutionalized conflict** occurs when a conflict factor is built into the organization.

III. **Conflict Analysis.** Anyone who wants to arbitrate a conflict needs to begin by looking closely at what is really happening. The following questions should be asked:

   A. Who is involved?

   B. What is at stake?

   C. How important is time?

   D. What are the tie-ins with other issues?

IV. **Potential Solutions**

   A. There are three possible solutions to a conflict: win–lose, lose–lose, and win–win.

   1. **Win–lose.** In this strategy, one side wins at the expense of the other.

   2. **Lose–lose.** In this strategy, both sides have to give up enough so that they both feel they have lost.

   3. **Win–win.** In win–win, both sides feel that they have come out as winners.

   B. Both the win–lose and lose–lose approaches tend to produce a negative side-taking mentality and are not likely to solve the problem.

   1. Win–lose usually involves one side of a conflict winning at the expense of the other. Two common types of win–lose approaches are:

      a. Democratic vote.

      b. Arbitrary approach.

   2. In the lose–lose strategy, everyone gives something up. The main approach in lose–lose is compromise.

V. Styles of Conflict Management

A. Another way to look at solutions to conflict is by using the Thomas–Kilman conflict model. (Refer students to Figure 13.2 in their textbooks.)

1. If you are a **competitor:** Competitors will likely try a win–lose approach to conflict resolution.

2. If you are an **avoider:** Avoiders would rather not be around conflict at all.

3. If you are a **compromiser:** Compromisers use their skills to blend differences to form a workable alternative. A compromiser should push for a win–win solution, following all the steps in that process.

4. If you are an **accommodator:** The accommodator wants to avoid conflict by positive thinking, telling people to "count their blessings" or "look on the bright side."

5. If you are a **collaborator:** Collaborators bring both sides together for discussion, and is most likely to bring about a win–win solution.

B. Qualities of an effective conflict resolution method. (Refer students to Figure 13.3 in their textbooks.) An effective conflict resolver does the following:

1. clarifies interests
2. builds a good working relationship
3. generates good opinions
4. is recognized by both sides as legitimate
5. improves communication
6. leads to wise commitments

VI. Dealing with Special Conflict Cases.
Problem people are individuals in an organization who are not living up to the expectations of the organization.

VII. Low Conformers

A. Conflicts with low conformers. **Low conformers** are people who have their own unique view of life and do not feel the need to conform in ways most people do. Here are some suggestions that will make working with low conformers less difficult:

1. Learn to tolerate their honesty.
2. Accept the low conformer's firm method of self-expression without calling it stubbornness or disloyalty.
3. Support low conformers when others are overly critical.
4. Accept their independence; don't be offended if they don't ask for your advice.
5. Resist the urge to ask them to come to conclusions.
6. Give relevant positive reinforcement even when they don't seem to need it.

B. Conflicts with envious people. Envy is wanting what another person has to the extent of feeling ill will toward that person. You should choose one or

more of the following approaches to find one that works:

1. Avoid destructive conflict with the envious person.
2. Confront the envious coworker.
3. Ignore the envious person.
4. Discuss the problem with your manager.

C. Conflicts with whiners and complainers. Whether you are the manager or coworker of a whiner or complainer, there are some steps you can take to deal with this common source of conflict:

1. Listen, but not too much.
2. Do frequent reality checks.
3. Challenge the word "unfair."
4. Be a team leader or player.

D. Conflicts with passive and unresponsive people. Unresponsive people react to any confrontation or potential conflict by shutting down. You can take some positive steps to get meaningful feedback:

1. Ask open-ended questions.
2. Develop and use a friendly, silent stare or gaze.
3. Don't fill the space. Rescued passives will remain passive.
4. Make brief statements to help break the tension.
5. Set time limits.

 13.1 Negotiate Win–Win Solutions. A win–win solution is when both sides feel they have come out on top. The conflict manager may use **concession bargaining**. The conflict group must go step-by-step through some important guidelines before the win–win method can work:

1. Get emotions under control.
2. Agree on ground rules.
3. Clarify all positions.
4. Explore multiple needs and issues.
5. Develop alternatives.
6. Choose the solutions that are win–win.

 13.2 Collaborate With Others. The collaborator should use a step-by-step conflict resolution method that includes four phases:

1. Identify the problem.
2. Generate a solution.
3. Identify an action plan.
4. Put the action plan to work.

 13.3 Stop Conflicts Before They Start. Managers and employees can take steps to prevent many conflicts and to soften the impact when they happen.

1. Turn the people around you into winners.
2. Work together on common goals.
3. Communicate, communicate, communicate.

PHOTO, page 401: Does Jeanne contribute to her unfavorable work conditions in any way? What can Jeanne do to improve the situation at work?

Yes. By not addressing the problem to those involved in the conflict, Jeanne prevents the conflict from being resolved. Jeanne can schedule a meeting with the marketing, production, and research and development departments to effectively resolve the conflict by opening up communication to satisfy each department's needs.

FIGURE 13.1, page 404: Which of these sources do you feel is easiest to confront and resolve?

Your answer will depend on your comfort levels when working with yourself and others. If you like the challenge of working on yourself, then inner conflicts will likely be easier for you to solve. If you like the challenge of debating and winning over other people, perhaps the other situations will be more satisfying for you.

PHOTO, page 406: What conflict do you feel is most common in organizations?

Negotiation-of-selves conflict is prevalent in any organization since it is the process of defining yourself to others and responding to their implied definitions of themselves. This type of conflict can focus on power or authority, personality traits, or on questions of duty and obligation.

PHOTO, page 411: How can people bring more win–win situations to their work environment?

Even if an organization understands the win–win solution very well, it can accomplish this solution more often by looking closely at where the problems are, who is unhappy and why, and where conflicts look like they are about to start. Win–win solutions encourage conflict prevention and efficient management.

FIGURE 13.2, page 412: With which style do you identify?

There is no right or wrong answer to this; it just depends on your personality. Many people have more than one style depending on the situation: whether you are at home or at work, with coworkers or your manager, may determine your style.

PHOTO, page 413: Why might the collaborator require the most skill and diplomacy of all the styles of managing conflict?

The collaborator brings both sides together for discussion and is most likely to bring about a win–win solution. The collaborator encourages communication to learn about each party's feelings, and values their opinions.

FIGURE 13.3, page 415: Can you think of other qualities of an effective conflict resolution method?

Answers will vary, but most likely they will reflect improved confidence in all parties involved, as well as in the organization's method of resolving conflict.

CHAPTER REVIEW, pages 428–434

Review Questions

❶ What are the major causes of conflict in the workplace?

This is an important question, because understanding the reasons why conflict exists is the first step in dealing with it. The primary reason for conflict in the workplace is that the workplace is made up of people, and wherever there are people there is conflict. The most important four sources, though, are covered in question #2.

❷ What are the four major sources of conflict within organizations? Explain each one, using an example.

1. Content conflict. This type of conflict comes from differences in understanding a concept, order, policy, etc. The two types of content conflict are those based on the existence of something, and those based on the meaning of something. Existence issues should be the easiest to deal with, because existence is usually provable. Meaning, however, can be very subjective. Imagine two electronics troubleshooters in a high-tech company. The policy of the company states that all reasonable attempts must be made to find the causes of computer viruses in the company system. Both troubleshooters have located and eliminated the virus, but now they are arguing about the phrase "all reasonable attempts" as it applies to finding out how it happened. One debugger argues that finding and eliminating the virus is adequate; the other interprets the phrase to involve prevention of further recurrence.

2. Values conflict. Values differences are less common than people often suspect, yet they are real. These conflicts often have to do as much with one

person's perception of the other's values as with the values themselves. The most important source of values conflicts is people's lack of tolerance for those with values different from their own. An example would be two people whose attitudes toward money are opposite: Charlie sees James as greedy and shallow, and James perceives Charlie as lazy and unambitious.

3. Negotiation-of-selves conflict. This is likely to be the trickiest source of conflict for students to understand. Socially, most people are in a constant process of defining themselves to others. Negotiation-of-selves is the type of conflict that emerges during that process. In addition, it is the source of conflict that is tied in most directly to self-esteem problems. Quite a bit of the material in Chapter 3, on self-disclosure and self-awareness, could easily be used to show how presentation of self can erode, with negotiation-of-selves conflict as the result.

4. Institutionalized conflict. When conflict factors seem to be built into an institution, this type of conflict is difficult to avoid. One perfect example is the two houses of the British Parliament—the House of Lords and the House of Commons. The very polarization of the two houses reflects the fact that the organization was built specifically for conflict—albeit constructive conflict.

Students could certainly go beyond the textbook and correctly identify other sources of workplace conflict. Personality clashes are definitely a subdivision of negotiation-of-selves. Polarization is a subdivision of larger conflicts; point out that polarization itself likely resulted from one of the four areas above, and continues to create more conflict.

❸ Explain the Thomas–Kilman Conflict Model. What does this model show as the best method of conflict resolution?

This model shows assertiveness and cooperation as the two points of reference.

Competitors tend to think of conflict in terms of win–lose. Thus, anything from a contest to a democratic vote will be likely used by this type to determine the "winner." If you have high assertiveness and low cooperation skills and attitudes, you will likely use the competitor approach to conflict management. You might also use arbitration, simply judging the situation personally. When this approach is taken, win–lose results are still likely.

If you have low assertiveness and low cooperation skills and attitudes, you will likely use the avoider approach and be tempted to escape. **Avoiders,** however, usually end up with the internal conflict of stress, even when they succeed in avoiding organizational conflict.

If your assertiveness skills and cooperation skills are both average, compromising may become your method of dealing with conflict. A **compromiser** uses negotiation skills to work out a solution that will involve both sides of the conflict giving up something. This solution is closer to lose–lose than win–win.

The **accommodator** can sometimes be confused with a compromiser or even a collaborator, but closer examination will prove otherwise. These types of people have low assertiveness skills but high cooperation skills, so they will be a "yes person" trying to please both sides. Like the avoider, the accommodator does not enjoy conflict, but he or she runs away from the conflict emotionally instead of physically.

The **collaborator** is the only type of conflict manager who is very likely to bring about a true win–win solution. With skills and attitudes high in both assertiveness and cooperation, this type takes a leadership role while still listening and motivating others to listen to each other.

❹ Is conflict always negative? If so, what are some effective ways of preventing destructive conflict in the workplace?

No. However, destructive conflict is likely to occur in any workplace. Fortunately, there are several ways to combat it. Possible solutions fall under three general categories: win–lose, lose–lose, and win–win. Win–win is widely considered the best approach because it encourages collaboration and solves problems at their root, rather than just focusing on compromise or a "winner-take-all" attitude that can create further division.

Six steps to create a win–win solution are:
1. Get emotions under control.
2. Agree on ground rules.
3. Clarify all positions.
4. Explore multiple needs and issues.
5. Develop alternatives.
6. Choose solutions that are win–win.

To achieve win–win, the best conflict management approach is that of the collaborator. The collaborator brings both sides together for discussion, sees conflict resolution as a problem-solving process, and will take the following steps to ensure that the solution is right for everyone:
1. Identify the problem.
2. Generate a solution.
3. Identify an action plan.
4. Put the action plan to work.

❺ You are trying to negotiate a workplace conflict through to a win–win solution. What steps would you follow? What pitfalls would you need to avoid?

Win-win is a method of getting at the basis of the real problem and fixing it permanently. As the conflict negotiator, you would first need to listen to all sides of the issue very carefully, taking notes unless you have an excellent memory. Then, define the basic issues and establish an atmosphere of trust among all involved. You will need to be sensitive, patient, and calm, which will require real self-discipline. Retain that self-discipline by reminding yourself that your goal is to get at the real root of the problem and to solve it once and for all.

❻ What is negotiation-of-selves conflict, and why is this source of conflict probably the most important in the workplace?

This type of conflict is based on differences in how people define themselves. Chapter 2 deals with self-concept. People usually define themselves on the basis of their self-concept, with the four parts discussed in that chapter (real self, ideal self, looking-glass self, and self-image).

If John talks to Jane as though he were her superior in terms of intellect, experience, wisdom, good looks, or whatever, and Jane rejects that implied evaluation, conflict results. In the workplace as well as elsewhere in life, people are constantly involved in negotiations-of-selves. It is probably the most important conflict in the workplace because it is by far the most pervasive.

❼ What should you do when a person who constantly complains confronts you? Why should you avoid being indifferent or ignoring the person? How would reality checks and being a team leader help?

1. Dealing with this type of problem person can be delicate. For one thing, you don't want to appear indifferent to the whiner. Indifference will usually only serve to reinforce the complaining that is already going on. That is why you should "listen, but not too much." Keep the person on track by asking these questions: "What is your point?" or "What are you really trying to tell me about the deadlines in the purchasing department" or whatever the exact issue might be.

2. Also, do frequent reality checks. Chronic complainers live in a reality where everything is going wrong and most of it is aimed at them. Do not let them pull you into that reality. The sentence mentioned in the text is: "OK, tell me exactly what the problem is and what you want me to do about it." That's a good standby. Keep the conversation dealing with objective reality—what the company and the world are really like.

3. Do not ignore—or automatically accept—the word "unfair." As mentioned in the last paragraph, these people live in a world of perceived unfairness. Often, it will be effective to force the complainer to define the term "unfair." Refine the definition to where it squares with reality, then use it to define the "unfairness" being discussed. Often, though, this will only shut the complainer up temporarily. Just make sure that this type of problem person knows there are limits to your tolerance of the complaining.

4. Be a team leader or player. When you promote teamwork in the workplace, chronic whiners and complainers will find that they need to either leave or join the team. Team players make constructive suggestions and do not complain.

❽ How can a manager or employee tell if they are dealing with a passive person? What is the best way to deal with the passive, close-mouthed person who is determined not to communicate?

This type of individual is usually called a passive or passive-aggressive person. This type often seems easygoing and agreeable on the surface. Discovering whether you are really dealing with a difficult person is often difficult when the passive person is involved, since not all quiet people are passives. Watch the person's behavior over a period of time, then, once you are convinced that you are dealing with a passive person, follow the steps in the textbook:

1. Ask open-ended questions. Closed-ended question will be answered with "Yeah, sure," "OK," "Whatever you say," etc. Open-ended questions force a response, which is the first step in getting past the passive behavior.

2. Develop and use a friendly, silent gaze. A quizzical, expectant expression can stimulate action in a passive person. It's a form of pressure they can only respond to with words or by leaving the conversation physically.

3. Don't fill the space. Learn to be comfortable with silence—from both of you. Don't give in to the temptation of thinking that your extra talking is going to "prime the pump." Usually, it won't.

4. Make statements to help break the tension. However, make sure you don't violate step #3 in doing so.

5. Set time limits. Tell the passive person what the time limit is; then stick to it.

Critical Thinking Questions

9 Try to remember a conflict you have had with someone recently. What were the sources of the conflict? Was the conflict ever resolved? If so, how? Would you resolve it differently if you could replay the event?

Answers will vary. For the last part of the question, ask students why they would resolve it differently, and how they would do so.

10 Have you ever tried to work or study with a difficult person, such as a whiner or envious person? How did you relate to that individual, if at all? Have you ever confronted an envious person? If so, what happened?

Answers will vary, but many students will report frustration, anger, and a sense of being manipulated. Many will state that they dealt with it by breaking away from the person, such as by no longer studying or socializing with them. Ask if anyone confronted the difficult person; if so, what happened?

INTERNET EXERCISES

Tips for Teachers

1. **Read and Write** Ask students who have read this chapter and done this exercise:
   - What elements in a conflict make it unavoidable?
   - What elements of your personality make you refuse to avoid certain conflicts (such as those over values)?

2. **Read and Write** Ask students how important is negotiation-of-selves when someone is beginning a new job or position. What experiences have they had in this respect, and do they feel there is a blanket cure for this type of usually unavoidable conflict?

Working It Out

13.1 Your Conflict Management Style

This exercise can work in discussion groups. If you choose this approach, divide the class into groups of four or five *after* they have completed the questionnaire individually. In an informal discussion, each group can discuss the differences in scores, whether they agree with the scores, and how they differ in basic attitudes toward conflict. The exercise also works well in class, followed by a general discussion or as a take-home assignment.

Case Study

13.1 The Wrenches and the Suits

1. What are the sources of the conflict in this case? Explain.

Notice how much **negotiation-of-selves** is going on here. Both sides have polarized on the basis of self-definition. Oddly enough, the way the two sides are forced to dress due to their occupations figures into the equation. Their perceived differences in status in the organization are also important. Nearly all of the conflict that doesn't come from negotiation-of-selves is **institutionalized conflict.** The fact that these two factions exist in many car dealerships shows this to be a widespread institutionalization of conflict. Students can also present a case for **values conflict,** since the values of the mechanical types tend to be considerably different from the values of the sales force.

2. Is Barry, the sales manager, the right person to be the conflict manager in this situation? Why or why not?

Barry is, after all, one of the suits; in fact, he is the chief of all suits. Therefore, even if he attempts to remain neutral, he will likely not be seen as such. He has a potential conflict of interests simply because the sales people are under his management. Barry's best bet is to find someone neutral—perhaps the owner of the franchise or a consultant hired by the company, not by the sales department.

Instead of doing any of this, Barry might be tempted to tell José, "That's just the way this business is." However, the case implies that José has worked at other dealerships and hasn't previously run into this degree of polarization. Whatever Barry decides to do, he needs to get a neutral party who will break down the walls that are causing counterproductive conflict.

3. What would you do if you were José? What will happen if Barry chooses to do nothing? Can José and his fellow salespeople do anything to effect a change? If so, what?

José cannot do as much initially as his supervisor or a consultant could, but there are some avenues of improvement open to him. He could start by calling a meeting of any interested members of both sides to talk about their differences. Some students will say that nobody would come to such a meeting—and that could

be true, because the hostility between these two groups is deep-seated.

If the meeting does take place, José should follow the guidelines for negotiating a win–win solution:

1. Get emotions under control.
2. Agree on ground rules.
3. Clarify all positions.
4. Explore multiple needs and issues.
5. Develop alternatives.
6. Choose the solutions that are win–win.

The discussion of this case can become very active, especially if the class contains students who have been in a situation such as this.

Case Study

13.2 The Rush Order

1. What are the sources of conflict in this case?

Negotiation-of-selves can explain much of the situation. First, Hans presents himself to the customer as a salesperson who can provide on demand a speedy—unreasonably speedy—order. He does so successfully, at least in the perception of his customer. Second, he presents himself to Norma as someone who deserves her full attention and some unreasonable accommodations. Here the negotiation-of-selves breaks down because Norma doesn't accept his negotiation. His third self-presentation is to Mr. Carlson. For reasons that the readers of the case can only guess, this negotiation breaks down as well.

At this point, Hans goes back for a renegotiation-of-selves with Norma. This negotiation doesn't break down because both sides are willing to continue this time, mostly owing to Hans' more humble attitude. His final renegotiation will be with Mr. Carlson. Assuming that this one goes well, the conflict will be terminated.

A values conflict is present as well: Hans has shown by his conduct that he values a sale over harmony with the people in his company. Perhaps the action of this case will force him to re-examine that value.

2. Is the solution a win–win? Explain?

A win–win solution is one in which both sides feel like winners. One could make a case that both sides feel like winners at the end of this case because both Norma and Hans received something close to what they wanted at the end. However, one can safely assume that Norma would be unlikely to repeat this exact scenario in the future. That assumption would force the reader to perceive her feeling of "winning" as being at least somewhat tempered. Also, if Hans has learned anything at all from this encounter, he will perceive that pulling this tactic again probably will not work, either with Norma or with Carlson. He should view the "victory" as a last-time concession. Thus, he's not feeling too much like a winner either.

Instead, this is closer to a lose–lose situation. Both sides have had to give something up. The major gain that Hans has to forfeit is his future use of the speedy-delivery sales tactic. Norma has had to give up her current schedule in order to put out a rush order that she would rather have avoided. Thus, she also has lost.

3. If Hans should come up with another situation like this one, what would you do if you were Norma? If you were Mr. Carlson?

In 2000 this case was tested and role-played for the group in a company training program. In the audience were several production managers who had experienced nearly identical situations with their sales force. They were the most adamant that Hans should be "on probation." If he should be so foolish as to break that probation, he would need some sort of discipline to prevent him from ever trying the tactic again.

Student replies will vary. Those who have worked in sales might be a bit more sympathetic toward Hans' position. You can use the discussion to reinforce some important points on conflict management contained in this chapter.

Stress and Stress Management

Chapter 14

LECTURE OUTLINE

I. Causes of Stress

A. Stress is the body's reaction to any demand made on it, and a stressor is the situation or event causing the stress.

B. There are two kinds of stress, eustress and distress, but your body's reaction to both of these is the same.

1. **Eustress**, or good stress, comes from pleasant, desirable events or situations, such as parties or holidays.

2. **Distress** is the harmful and negative kind of stress that comes from unpleasant sources, such as divorce, a speeding ticket, or a death in the family. (Note: The text will only refer to distress from this point on as stress, since that is the more common conception of stress.)

C. Sources of stress, or **stressors**, include:

1. **Major life changes**, including events such as a death in the family, the birth of a child, or a new job.

2. **Daily hassles**, such as losing your keys or getting a parking ticket. These can pile up and worsen your feelings of stress. They can occur as a result of major life changes.

3. **Chronic stressors** include the day-to-day things you cannot easily escape, such as poverty, a chronic illness, racism and other types of discrimination, or an abusive relationship.

4. **External stressors** include pain, **frustration**, crowding, and inner conflict. **Inner conflict** is actually a type of external stress because the source of the conflict comes from outside the person. Three types of inner conflict are:

   a. Approach–approach situations, where you want two things but must choose between them.

   b. Approach–avoid situations, where you feel conflict when making a decision between avoiding an unpleasant outcome and reaching a desirable goal.

   c. Avoid–avoid situations, where you must choose between two undesirable outcomes.

5. **Internal stressors** are the stress you create within yourself, through your perception of events or your personality-related behaviors.

   a. **Cognitive appraisal** is your evaluation of the stress level of each event, and your perception of whether you can handle the stressor.

   b. **Irrational belief systems** are those that increase stress, such as the belief that everyone must like you and you must not make mistakes. These can lead you to **catastrophize**, which is blowing things out of proportion and increasing your feelings of stress.

II. Type A and Type B Personalities

A. Type A personality-related behaviors include hostility, anger, and a sense of time urgency; these behaviors are linked with stress-related illnesses.

B. Type B personality-related behaviors include calm, contentment, lowered time urgency, and less risk of stress-related illness.

C. Another type of personality is the **hardy personality**, or resilient personality, characterized by the ability to meet challenges, a sense of commitment, and a feeling of being in control of life.

III. The Physical Effects of Stress

A. Hans Selye's General Adaptation Syndrome (G.A.S.) is a three-stage theory that describes what stress does to people physically:

1. Alarm stage, or what is now called "fight or flight response," is the first stage, in which the autonomic nervous system is aroused. Heart rate, respiration, and perspiration increase, and adrenaline is released.

2. Stage of adaptation is characterized by resistance, in which the body is fighting the stressor and bodily reactions are still above normal.

3. Stage of exhaustion occurs only if the stressor remains and the body's resources are used up (or exhausted). The risk of illness, accidents, fatigue, or death increases in this stage.

B. Stress and the immune system

1. Stress reduces the immune system functions of recognizing antigens, fighting them, and remembering them for later detection.

2. Stress-related illnesses (e.g., heart attacks) are the result of prolonged exposure to stress.

3. Techniques for reducing stress reactions include progressive relaxation, biofeedback, and meditation.

IV. **The Cost of Stress in the Workplace**

A. Stress-related problems cost the American economy $75-150 billion dollars each year.

B. Stress-related physical complaints are rising. Employees are pointing to poor management practices and work environments as the causes.

C. Stress also reduces self-esteem, which worsens stress-related illness and productivity.

 14.1 Discard Irrational Beliefs

1. Evaluate the consequences of the belief.

2. Identify your belief system.

3. Dispute the self-defeating belief.

4. Practice effective ways of thinking.

 14.2 Change Your Personality. You can change behaviors associated with personality types. Changing these behaviors will help you to reduce stress and maintain health.

1. Take charge of your life.

2. Use humor.

3. Compare yourself to others.

4. Take advantage of stress.

5. Learn to live with unavoidable stress.

 14.3 Take Care of Yourself

1. Use relaxation techniques.

2. Increase your fitness: Exercise, eat well, and reduce/quit smoking and drinking.

3. Make time for rest and leisure.

4. Get social support.

5. Try to reduce stress in the workplace.

6. Manage your time.

7. Stop **procrastinating**!

ANSWERS TO IN-CHAPTER QUESTIONS

PHOTO, page 437: How do you think Patrick should address Zane's outburst? What do you do when dealing with people who overreact?

Patrick should have a discussion with Zane to learn the cause of Zane's stress. Students' answers will vary based on their personality types.

PHOTO, page 439: How do you deal with those days when "nothing seems to go right"?

There are several different ways to deal with daily hassles, as you'll learn later in this chapter. They include dealing with your emotional stress and anxiety, as well as discarding irrational beliefs that prolong stress—such as the idea that a day that starts badly will continue that way no matter what.

FIGURE 14.1, page 444: How much can your beliefs affect the outcome of stressful situations?

They can affect it greatly: What you believe you can or cannot accomplish in a stressful situation often becomes the case.

FIGURE 14.2, page 445: What are your irrational beliefs, and what do they do to your stress level?

Irrational beliefs are often unconscious, so it is sometimes hard to pinpoint them. After some self-examination, many people realize that they hold quite a few of the irrational beliefs listed here. Irrational beliefs often cause stress levels to rise.

PHOTO, page 446: How can you get rid of self-defeating beliefs?

Probably the best way is to argue against them. Question the belief and see if it holds up; if it is irrational, it will not.

PHOTO, page 452: What do you do to strengthen your body against stress?

Most people will cite the factors listed above, and some might mention others such as meditation, yoga, and other relaxation techniques.

FIGURE 14.3, page 453: What can your current (or most recent) manager do to reduce stress at his or her workplace?

Managers can take any of the suggestions listed here and apply them to their situation on an as-needed basis. Remember that many of these issues are related, and improvement in one area will often lead to improvement in another.

PHOTO, page 455: How does a stressful situation in one part of your life (such as work) affect the other parts?

Since stress affects you physically, enduring stress at work can carry over into your overall well-being at home, school, or elsewhere. The emotional and psychological effects are far-reaching as well.

FIGURE 14.4, page 456: Which of these principles seems most important to you?

Your answer will depend on your past experiences, as well as your ability to handle different types of stress. If you have found yourself overwhelmed by overly large workloads in the past and dread encountering that again in the future, then perhaps principle #1 is most important to you. If, however, you felt that the cause of the heavy workload was a chaotic office in which labor wasn't managed efficiently and work wasn't delegated effectively, then principle #2 may be more important.

Review Questions

① What is meant by stress and stressors? Identify two sources of eustress, and two sources of distress, in your own life.

Stress is the body's reaction to any demand made on it, and a **stressor** is the situation or event causing the stress. Stress can be caused by events you perceive as pleasant (**eustress**) or unpleasant (**distress**). What most people refer to as stress is distress. Most people don't usually tend to think of pleasant events as stressful, although the physical effects are the same for both. Some stress is necessary to keep you stimulated and active; without any stress (i.e., external stimulation), you would be completely unmotivated and could die.

Answers regarding sources of distress and eustress will vary, but students must demonstrate that events perceived as pleasant are sources of eustress, while unpleasant events are sources of distress.

② How are major life changes different from daily hassles? How can a major life change lead to daily hassles? Discuss examples of these in your own life.

Examples will vary. Major life changes include events that affect a person's life status, e.g., marriage, divorce, or college graduation; or events that drastically affect a person's life, e.g., a serious illness or a criminal conviction. Daily hassles are the small annoyances that are encountered each day that add stress to a person's life, e.g., car trouble, traffic, or minor illnesses.

Major life changes can cause disruptions in routine that lead to daily hassles; e.g., buying a new home means having to find a new grocery store, a new route to work, and so on.

③ Suppose that you were really looking forward to going to work one day, but when you left for work you realized your tire was flat. Your stress level increased. Discuss how this situation leads to internal and/or external sources of stress.

Since the situation originated from external sources, it is categorized as an **external stressor**. However, your perception of this event as a catastrophe while in the process of cognitively appraising this event will lead to internal stress. A perception of the flat tire as just a minor annoyance will reduce your internal stress in this situation.

④ Are there any chronic stressors in your own life, or the life of someone you know? Describe the stressor, and possible coping strategies.

Chronic stressors are day-to-day things that cause stress from which the person cannot escape. They would include such things as a chronic illness, living in a dangerous neighborhood, poverty, being in an abusive relationship, racism, sexism, and working at a job in which you have no control or decision-making power.

Possible coping strategies include changing your perception or cognitive appraisal of the event (for example, seeing it as less of a problem and not letting it get out of hand), using meditation or progressive relaxation, increasing your overall fitness so that less physical damage can occur, making time for rest or leisure away from the stressor, maintaining social support networks, and managing your time effectively to reduce unnecessary stress. Some people may cope best by looking for the humor in a situation, taking charge of their lives, comparing themselves to others who are worse off, taking advantage of some stress as a motivating factor, and learning to live with unavoidable stress without letting it take over.

⑤ Do you hold any of the irrational beliefs described by Ellis? How do they affect your perception of events?

According to Ellis, everyone holds at least some irrational beliefs. The top ten irrational beliefs identified by Ellis include beliefs that people must like you; you must be competent; others who act unfairly are bad people; frustrating situations are catastrophic; emotional misery comes from outside the self; you must obsess about dangerous situations; avoiding problems is better than facing them; it is horrible if you can't find good solutions to life's problems; and you can achieve maximum happiness by inertia. Ellis would say that these irrational beliefs allow people to catastrophize, which increases stress; therefore, they are a source of stress in themselves.

⑥ According to Ellis, what is catastrophizing? Do you ever find yourself catastrophizing? In what situations? How can you minimize it?

Catastrophizing, from Ellis's A-B-C theory of irrational beliefs and stress, is turning a stressful situation (no matter how minor) into a catastrophe. In short, it is blowing things out of proportion. The slogan for people who catastrophize would be: "Make mountains out of molehills." Ellis said it is your perception of events, not the events themselves, that causes stress.

Ellis believed that most people catastrophize at one time or another, depending on the situation. The trick to minimizing the harmful effects of irrational beliefs that lead to catastrophizing is to re-evaluate the consequences you believe are true about the event, then identify and confront your beliefs, replacing irrational beliefs with more rational ones.

❼ What is the difference between meditation and biofeedback? How can each be used to reduce stress? What other specific suggestions for coping with stress can you incorporate into your own life?

Meditation is a technique (or group of techniques) that enables you to increase outward or inward focus, blocking out external stimuli. Meditation allows you to learn to control your mind by stopping it from wandering. By meditating, you can learn to relax and even change body processes. People use meditation to lower their blood pressure, and to control body processes such as heart rate, respiration, and body temperature. **Biofeedback** is a process in which people learn to recognize when they are producing a specific body reaction, by getting constant feedback from a biofeedback machine to which they are attached. Paying attention to this feedback allows them to learn to control those body reactions or responses.

People can learn to use both meditation and biofeedback to relax and avoid strong negative physical reactions to stressors.

Answers regarding specific coping strategies will vary, but may include increasing overall fitness, using other relaxation techniques, taking time for rest and leisure, maintaining social support networks, taking steps to reduce stress in the workplace, and managing time more effectively.

❽ Suppose you are driving to work one day on your usual route past the City Zoo, when a giant grizzly bear escapes, runs out of the entrance, growling and roaring, and heads straight for your car. Describe the physical and chemical changes that you would experience, according to the general adaptation syndrome (G.A.S.).

The three stages of G.A.S. are alarm, resistance, and exhaustion. Alarm would occur when you realize the bear is loose and is heading for your car. This would trigger the arousal of the sympathetic branch of the autonomic nervous system (A.N.S.) and result in an increase in heartrate, respiration, perspiration, muscle tension, stomach acid, adrenaline release, and all of the other biochemical changes associated with "fight or flight."

Once these changes have occurred, you would enter the second stage, resistance. In this stage, you are resisting the stressor by taking whatever steps are necessary to

confront it or escape it. In this case, you will probably try to escape. During this stage, bodily responses such as breathing and sweating are still above normal, and you are more vulnerable if another stressor appears. Most people successfully cope with stressors during this stage, and the parasympathetic system then becomes aroused while the sympathetic system begins to relax; this means that your body's responses will return to normal.

If the threat of the bear continues, and your body's resources have been used up, you will no longer be able to maintain the resistance to the bear. You will then enter the third stage of G.A.S. In this stage, your body's resources and your ability to resist are used up, or exhausted. In the exhaustion stage, you are in danger of fatigue, accidents, illnesses, and death.

Critical Thinking Questions

❾ A life without stress seems like a pleasant and desirable goal. Do you agree with Selye that stress is necessary in order to motivate you and keep you alive? Why or why not? What do you think would happen if you didn't have any stress in your life?

Answers will vary depending on how students interpret the concept of stress. If they interpret it literally as Selye meant it, as any change that your body must adapt to, then you do need stress to keep your body functioning normally. Students who interpret this concept as distress only may disagree with Selye and state that a life without stress sounds wonderful.

❿ Some people say that since everyone is going to die anyway, it would be better to enjoy life without worrying about diet, exercise, and other behaviors that may prolong life while reducing the enjoyment of life. Why do you think these people feel this way? What do you think?

Answers will vary according to students' long-term goals. Some students may prefer a pleasurable (but possibly shorter and less healthful) life versus a longer and more healthful (but more boring) life. Other students may prefer a longer and possibly less exciting life. A good answer to this question includes the point that it is difficult to enjoy life if one is ill, abusing substances, morbidly obese, or otherwise not taking care of one's health.

Working It Out

14.1 Type A and Type B Personality Behaviors

This activity is nice for getting students engaged in a discussion about the behaviors that indicate whether they are time urgent and maybe even hostile. It's interesting to see that students with the most time urgent behaviors often become irritated with filling out a survey that has no real "right" or "wrong" answers. They tend to think it is a waste of time, although they are the students who need to hear this message the most! This activity can also spark student debate about personality versus behaviors: how rigid *are* your personality behaviors? (Remind them that behavior patterns are just habits that can be changed.)

Many students (typically those with a high Type A score) will also argue that Type A behavior is helpful in getting ahead and getting things done. Remind them that this belief is not in dispute; it's just that the anger and hostility, along with the constant sense of time urgency, create stress and are damaging to health.

Working It Out

14.2 Stress Self-Test

This test is a good way to get students to reflect on the damage that stress may be doing to their quality of life (in the short term) and their life expectancy (in the long term). Make sure they learn the valuable lesson that physical complaints they believe are unavoidable (such as headache, sleep problems, or indigestion) may be under their complete control after all.

■ INTERNET EXERCISES

Tips for Teachers

1. **Read and Write** Discuss burnout in greater detail with your students; with today's ever-changing job market and the high burnout rate in many fields (such as technology), it is a relevant subject. In their experience, how much was too much—in other words, when did a stressful situation begin to create

unavoidable burnout? You can also ask if anyone ever succeeded in fighting off or reversing burnout. If so, what were the factors in place that enabled them to do this?

2. **Self-Assess and Apply** As an alternate or additional exercise, ask students to volunteer stress-reducing tips of their own.

Case Study

14.1 Bonnie the Bumblebee

1. Is James correct—will he more likely make it to upper management, or will Bonnie? Why?

James is probably thinking that Bonnie will suffer from a stress-related illness and will have to step down, while he will continue to work, get promotions and maintain good health. His steady, temperate pace causes him less stress and less damage to his immune system. In addition, since Bonnie is often "stinging" or hostile, she is probably alienating members of upper management, while James is not.

2. Thinking of the personality behaviors discussed in this chapter, what characteristics would lead you to categorize Bonnie and James as either Type A, Type B, or hardy?

Bonnie has the Type A behaviors of hostility and time urgency. James has more Type B behaviors: He is less intense and more laid back. He might also have hardy or resilient personality behaviors such as seeing problems as challenges, feeling in control of his life, and being committed to a cause or interest, but the reader doesn't have enough information here to know that.

3. Does Bonnie seem stressed? If so, from what sources (major life changes, daily hassles, chronic stressors, internal stress, or external stress)? If not, why not?

Yes, Bonnie seems stressed. The sources are probably internal, since no particular life changes or crises seem to have occurred and she is always behaving in this way. In addition, students may note that James is in the same work environment as Bonnie, but does not respond in the same way as she does.

Her personality behaviors and perceptions seem to be the sources of her stress. She perceives problems as more important or serious than they are. These internal perceptions are causing her stress level to rise and probably causing physical damage in the process.

Case Study

14.2 What's Wrong with Me?

1. What is wrong with Stephanie? If you were Lakeesha, what would you suggest is the problem ?

Stephanie is suffering from the effects of stress, which are probably caused by a combination of major life changes (divorce) and daily hassles (her children's illnesses and injuries, and financial problems due to late child support payments). In Stephanie's case, the major life change of divorce also probably contributed to the daily hassles. For example, she has to take time off of work for her children's medical appointments, a responsibility she may have shared with her husband while she was still married.

The effects of the stressors include the physical symptoms of insomnia and loss of appetite, and the behavioral symptoms of poor job performance and anger at her children. She is in the third stage of G.A.S., exhaustion, because she has become vulnerable to other stressors, such as viruses.

2. What job resources might Stephanie use to solve her problems?

Stephanie should find out through her supervisor what resources are available to her. These may include employee programs such as counseling, financial assistance, medical referrals, day care placements or referrals for her children, legal referrals for her financial or other problems, fitness or wellness programs, relaxation training, humor programs, and leave of absence programs. She may be able to modify her work hours to fit her family's schedule better through flextime, job sharing, telecommuting, or compressed workweeks.

(Note: Not all suggested responses to this question will be readily apparent from reading the text material, but students should be able to think of responses from their own or others' experiences.)

3. What kinds of actions could Stephanie take on her own to help herself?

In addition to investigating company resources and taking actions to help her situation in that way, Stephanie could take action with the suggestions listed in Strategy 14.3 (Take Care of Yourself). These include learning to relax through progressive relaxation or meditation; increasing her fitness by watching what she eats, stopping smoking and drinking, and getting plenty of exercise; building time into her schedule for rest and leisure activities; getting social support from her family, friends, coworkers, and possibly a support group; and learning to manage her time better.

ADDITIONAL ACTIVITIES

How to Meditate for Stress Reduction

This exercise will teach students to use simple, standard meditation techniques to aid in reducing everyday distress. Meditation can be accomplished using any one of several popular methods. The following instructions include the general steps to successful meditation to achieve relaxation, reduce stress, and increase overall health of mind and body.

You can teach this meditation technique in class, in a darkened and quiet room in which you will have no interruptions or distractions. If your classroom cannot be made dark and quiet, arrange to meet in another location. The exercise will take 15–20 minutes.

1. Find a calm and quiet environment where you will not be interrupted or distracted.
2. Find a comfortable physical position so that you will not experience muscle tension as you continue to release all thoughts.
3. Pick a mental device on which to concentrate or focus: This can be a word or a sound that you repeat over and over to yourself, either out loud or silently. Some common words are "one" or "ohm." It can also be an object that you concentrate on, such as a candle flame, flower, or vase.
4. Release all thoughts and let your mind take on a passive attitude. If you become distracted or your mind starts to wander, start concentrating again on your mental device.

After students have experienced a brief meditation session, encourage them to practice meditating 10–20 minutes twice a day for the best physical long-term effects.

Fight Procrastination

One of the biggest stress-inducing problems in managing time is procrastination, or putting things off until the last minute. The stress builds as you get closer and closer to the deadline, and finally you are faced with a momentous task to do in a short period of time that could have been completed easily in manageable chunks over a longer period.

Why do people procrastinate? Dr. David Burns suggests that there are both obvious and hidden benefits to procrastinating. Some obvious benefits are that:

- it's easy.
- it's a way to avoid frustration and anxiety.
- you can do other things that are more fun.
- you really don't want to do the task right now and don't have to, so you tell yourself it will get done sooner or later anyway.

Hidden benefits might be:

- revenge against people who are pressuring and making demands on you.
- getting someone else to do the work instead.
- showing people that you are already overwhelmed, so they won't make any new demands.
- getting out of doing things that are unpleasant and thus feeling special, like a king or queen.

Dr. Burns believes that procrastinating is a choice that people make knowingly and intentionally. Can you beat procrastination and manage your time better, and reduce your stress while doing so? Dr. Burns believes you can and suggests five steps:

1. **Get started** (or, as a popular advertisement says, "Just do it!"). Don't wait for motivation to come to you. Take action first, and motivation will follow.

2. **Make a specific plan.** When you have a task to complete, don't tell yourself you'll get started one of these days. Instead, make a plan: Will you start today? What time? What pieces of the task will you complete first?

3. **Make the job easier by breaking it down into little steps.** Start with 10 or 15 minutes of work on the task. Instead of believing you have to do it all at once and then feeling overwhelmed, tell yourself that you only have to do one small step at a time, and maybe only one step a day. After you have done your piece for that day, you can either quit for the day with a clear conscience or decide to do more.

4. **Think positive thoughts.** Write down negative thoughts that are making you feel anxious and substitute more positive and reasonable thoughts. (This is another way of saying that you should substitute rational for irrational beliefs.)

5. **Give yourself credit for work you have done.** Instead of feeling like a failure and putting yourself down for what you did not get done or for work you feel was not good enough, give yourself credit for the work you did do. Calling yourself a failure or a poor employee will only reduce your self-esteem, and that will make you even more likely to procrastinate in the future.

[SOURCE: David Burns, M.D., *Ten Days to Self-Esteem* (New York, NY: Morrow, 1993).]

Winning and Keeping Your Customers

Chapter 15

LECTURE OUTLINE

I. What Do Customers Really Want? If you want to be successful with customers, you must be sensitive to their emotional reactions. You also should leave them with good feelings.

  A. Your company needs the repeat customer—the loyal customer—to survive in the competitive 21st century.

  B. Customers buy only two things: **good feelings and solutions** to problems.

   1. Everything that a customer wants from you will fall into one of those two categories.

   2. Make those two categories the most important goals and activities you perform.

   3. What are the customer's real feelings?

II. Customer Service: A Definition

  A. "You have good service only when customers think you do." —John Tschohl, customer service expert.

  B. Good service, which always includes good human relations, is the main reason for repeat business.

  C. The average disgruntled customer tells eight to ten other people about the unpleasant experience.

III. The Two Simplest Principles of Customer Service

  A. Find out what the customer needs.

  B. Do whatever is necessary to satisfy that need.

   1. Learning to listen carefully is the most important part of this process.

   2. Avoid the tendency to oversimplify customer needs.

   3. Each customer has basic human needs that all people share in some measure. (Refer students to Figure 15.1.)

IV. Issues in Customer Service

  A. When delivering bad news, using sound **bad news skills** will help.

   1. Use a polite tone of voice.

   2. Don't spend excessive amounts of time on apologies.

   3. Explain *why* the problem exists.

   4. Speak to the customer about what can be done to solve the problem.

   5. If possible, don't say, "It's against company policy." The expression is trite, and it means very little to the customer.

  B. Encourage customer complaints.

   1. Don't make the incorrect assumption that if anything is wrong, the customer will say so.

   2. Learn to focus on the problem, then ask yourself, "What can I do that will solve the problem as this person sees it?"

   3. Try to influence everyone in your company to think of complaining customers in a positive way.

   4. Complaints from customers can make you aware of methods of improving service that would otherwise never have occurred to you.

   5. Phrase questions in a way that will encourage open and honest answers.

   6. Most important of all, make sure that you work as hard as you can to correct the problems that are causing customer complaints.

   7. **Nice customers** would be more helpful if they provided feedback.

V. Handling the Difficult Customer. Remember two things when dealing with an unreasonable, angry, or overly demanding customer.

  A. First, stay focused.

  B. Second, avoid the **self-esteem trap**; don't take the attack personally, and especially don't let it affect your own self-esteem.

VI. Going the Extra Mile. Courtesy, which is going the extra distance, nearly always pays for itself with returning customers and good referrals.

VII. Using Strong Ethics

A. Are you treating the customer in the way you would like to be treated in a similar situation?

B. By following the philosophy that the customer's needs are of greatest importance, much of the ethics issue will take care of itself.

VIII. Who Is Running the Business?

A. One final point must be made clear: You must set limits as to the extent to which you will allow a customer to run your business.

B. Regardless of how important the customer should be, he or she must *never* be allowed to undermine company decisions.

Strategy for Success **15.1 Establish a Bond With the Customer**

Relationship selling is forming meaningful relationships with your customers, which makes them more likely to return and buy from you again.

Three principles to help you form a bond of trust include the following:

1. Understand the customer's real needs.

2. If your customer is another business, learn about that business.

3. Provide exceptional service.

Strategy for Success **15.2 Support the Customer's Self-Esteem**

Nearly every customer you meet both wants and needs to have his or her self-esteem built up. Help customers like themselves better, and they will be much more likely to love—and buy—your products and services.

Here are some steps you can take to build up your customers' self-esteem:

1. Put the customer at ease. Smile, use the customer's name, try to use mannerisms like the customer, and try to get the customer relaxed and comfortable.

2. Put yourself in the customer's place. Empathize with your customer's concerns.

3. Make the customer feel understood. Listen effectively, communicate, and strive to understand the customer completely.

4. Make the customer feel important. Give your full attention, nothing else is as important as the customer!

5. Praise the customer appropriately. Do so in the framework of really caring, and make the praise specific.

Strategy for Success **15.3 Handling the Difficult Customer Professionally**

1. Let the customer vent: Being a good listener—even to an angry, perhaps ranting customer—is still the best approach.

2. Get the facts: Have all available information on the case right in front of you. In all cases, focus on what can be done to solve the problem, rather than on placing blame.

3. Be sure you understand the customer's feelings: What you see as the main issue might not at all be what the customers thinks it is.

4. Suggest a solution: Be specific and clear. Also, be careful not to make promises that your company might not let you keep.

5. End positively: Your main purpose in this last step is to keep the customer for future business.

6. Don't expect to win them all: Some customers are simply difficult people and will stay that way no matter what you do.

ANSWERS TO IN-CHAPTER QUESTIONS

PHOTO, page 475: What makes the Les Schwab Tire Center so successful? Are their policies applicable to other businesses?

The business is very successful because they treat the customer with respect and consideration, listening to what he or she has to say. Yes, good service is applicable to any business.

FIGURE 15.1, page 479: How many of these needs do you feel when you are making a purchase?

You may feel all of these at different times. Perhaps when you are making an everyday purchase like groceries you feel them less, while a major purchase like a car brings them out more strongly.

PHOTO, page 480: How can you learn more about the businesses with which you work?

Keeping abreast of the company's growth, news within its industry, and other details will help make you appear knowledgeable and trustworthy to customers.

FIGURE 15.2, page 482: How can you help customers understand the options available?

Explain the situation and why the problem exists. Try to not just say, "It's company policy," but instead give real reasons. After that, offer the options available and then discuss them with the customer. Usually, at that point the customer will reach an agreement with you.

FIGURE 15.3, page 484: What is a good way to help the nice customer let you know his or her true feelings?

By encouraging complaints in a pro-active manner, you can bring many customers out of their shells. By directly asking what you could do to make their experience better, you are asking customers for a specific answer. This will make them feel that their opinions count and will increase their trust in your company. Remember, though, to follow up on all reasonable requests.

PHOTO, page 485: What are ways to support a customer's self-esteem?

There are several ways, some of which are shown in Strategy 15.2. All of them have to do with creating a sense of ease and comfort, along with empathizing with the customer's needs.

FIGURE 15.4, page 485: How can these ideas help you keep the customer in perspective?

They help by reminding you that you need to generate trust and loyalty among customers in order to win their repeat business and survive.

PHOTO, page 486: Can all difficult customers be pleased?

No; some will be difficult no matter what you do to try to please them. However, you can make the situation as good as possible by treating them in a professional and helpful manner. Although it is tempting to argue, it will only make the situation worse.

FIGURE 15.5, page 488: When did a company "going the extra mile" make you want to stay their customer?

Your answer will depend on your experience, but most likely you remember feeling a pleasant surprise at seeing them do something "they didn't have to" just to create a feeling of trust.

CHAPTER REVIEW, pages 497–503

Review Questions

❶ Explain what it means to say that customers really want *feelings* and *solutions*, rather than products and services. When you are a customer, what does that mean to you?

These issues address the real needs, especially the emotional needs, of customers. When customers are unhappy, it is usually because these needs have not been met, although the customers themselves might not articulate their unhappiness in that way. By concentrating on these real needs—feelings and solutions—anyone dealing with customers will have greater success. Thus, anyone who deals with customers should ask, "What feelings is this person really after?" and, "What problems does he or she want to have solved?"

❷ Why is an understanding of the "nice" customer of great importance in improving customer service? Have you ever known or been someone like this "nice" customer, who is unhappy but only leaves and never returns?

Many people expect that if others are unhappy, they will let them know. The fact is that a very large number of customers and would-be customers are like the "nice" person featured in the textbook. The most important skill to learn in this connection is to assume that people are offended when something happens to offend them—even if they do not show their feelings. More importantly, you should prevent the offending incident from happening in the first place.

❸ What are the "two simplest principles" of customer service? What importance does listening play in the use of those principles? Have you ever seen them violated?

The two simplest principles are to:

1. Find out what the customer needs.

2. Do whatever is necessary to fulfill that need.

The principles might not be quite as simple as they seem, because customers often have multiple needs. Listening carefully and asking empathic questions will help in discovering what those needs are.

❹ Explain the importance of forming a bond with the customer. How does one go about establishing such a bond?

If you form a meaningful, real relationship with a customer, the improved results in repeat business should be obvious. Most people would rather do business with someone they like and trust. The following steps from the text can help:

1. Understand your customer's real needs. The key word here is "real." As already mentioned, customer's needs are not always readily apparent. The best way to evaluate those needs is by listening and asking questions.

2. If your customer is another business, learn about that business. Your interest in the customer's business not only gives you a leading edge in confidence, but the knowledge of the needs of the other business will likely help you serve its needs more completely.

3. Provide exceptional service. Exceptional service creates the strongest bond of all.

4. Don't be insincere. You can be genuinely polite and helpful even to someone whom you personally dislike. You can even form a bond with someone whose personality seems totally incompatible with yours. By providing exceptional service, you can help build a bond of trust and respect, even where there is no natural affection.

❺ What are the four steps in giving the customer bad news? Explain each step.

1. Use a polite tone of voice.

2. Don't spend an excessive amount of time on apologies. Customers usually prefer results to words.

3. Deal with why the problem exists. If you don't know, tell the customer you'll find out, and then really do it.

4. Speak to the customer about what can be done to solve the problem. This includes options for the customer, when possible. It also might include alternatives to options that aren't possible.

❻ What are some steps one can take to build the customer's self-esteem? Which step, in your opinion, is the most important? Explain.

These hints from the text can help build customer self-esteem.

1. Put the customer at ease. A relaxed customer who doesn't feel out of place is less likely to feel his or her self-esteem challenged in other areas.

2. Put yourself in the customer's place. Using empathy helps your customer feel appreciated. Ask yourself how you would feel if you were in a given customer's place: What would you want from the company?

3. Make the customer feel understood. Listening is the most important component here: Listen carefully, paying attention to nonverbal behaviors. Ask questions for clarity whenever you are even suspicious that you don't understand what the customer really means.

4. Make the customer feel important. Don't allow distractions to keep the customer from getting your full attention.

5. Praise the customer appropriately. Most of all, be sincere, and don't overdo this; an undue amount of praise can seem plastic and phony.

Students may offer a variety of reasons why they chose a certain step as the most important one to build the customer's self esteem.

❼ What is the importance of ethics in the treatment of customers? In what situations might ethics be used?

Ethics can make or break a sale, a series of sales, and even a company. A couple of ethics tests are used in the chapter, and several more are presented in Chapter 17. When you reach Chapter 17, you might want to refer back to the ethics issue in this chapter. One of the problems in dealing face-to-face with customers, as people must do in retailing, is that you sometimes are forced to make ethical choices quickly—on your feet, so to speak. Having an ethics test ready for use at such times can be most helpful. Whether it's the Golden Rule, the categorical imperative, or some other rule, know how to apply it and be prepared.

8 What is meant by "going the extra mile?" Provide an example from your life of either serving customers or being a customer. How did your experience affect you? Was there ever a time when someone didn't go the extra mile?

"Going the extra mile" simply means adding a small extra touch that will make your encounter with the customer remembered as something special. For instance, the customer asks for a favor—something above and beyond what should be expected. Assuming it's not going to cost a lot, do it with a smile: The smile is the extra mile. Besides being courteous and kind, it's simply good business. It's publicity-free marketing by word-of-mouth.

You might ask students to share an incident that stands out in their mind when they were customers and someone went the extra mile for them. Then discuss what all of the experiences had in common.

Critical Thinking Questions

9 Try to recall if you can identify a businessperson who was able to establish a bond with you or one of your family members. How was this accomplished?

Students may mention ways in which a businessperson performed extra services, showed extra friendliness or empathy, or did other "extras" that created a sense of trust and caring. This was probably accomplished through honest, down-to-earth communication; the businessperson's ability to learn about the customer's needs; and a consistent friendly and professional attitude.

Overall, the concept for developing such a bond is simple: Just remember that customers are human beings, and are as likely to have self-esteem deficiencies as anyone else. Because they are in the position of being the customer, that problem is likely a bit greater than usual. Customers need to feel that they are important to you. They expect and need to have your attention, and not be ignored. LeBoeuf is quoted in the text saying, "Help them to like themselves better, and they'll love you."

10 Have you ever been the victim of a company's poor customer service policy? What specifically occurred? How did this treatment make you feel? What would you have changed in that situation if you had the power to do so?

Nearly every student will be able to name incidents in which they received poor customer service, and some are worse than others. Some incidents will be the result of plain rudeness, and others will result from deceit, incompetence, or indifference. Be sure that this discussion, which can be lively, does not take up too much class time; you may want to decide on a time limit of, for instance, 10 minutes before calling on students for answers.

Most students will state that they would change the company's customer service training, as well as the company's methods for monitoring employee customer service skills. In addition, they will probably feel that the company should have done more to provide avenues for complaints and redress. Many students will report a feeling of anger, resentment, and helplessness, and their answers will reflect ways of addressing these issues.

■ INTERNET EXERCISES

Tips for Teachers

1. **Identify and Solve**   Ask students how they would (or have, in the past) counterbalanced their own self-esteem needs with those of an unhappy customer. Do they believe that this creates a common bond that can lead to mutual empathy? Discuss.

2. **Read and Write**   Some companies, such as trendy restaurants, are often quite unaccommodating to customers, and sometimes offer poor service because the sheer volume of business they receive makes them feel that it is a lowered priority. Ask your students for specific examples of how companies like this can avoid going from trendy to has-beens by improving their service skills.

Working It Out

15.1 The Difficult Customer

This exercise can work well for discussion but also works nicely as a role-play, especially if you can find a student who can play the character of the dog owner. Find a talented role player for that part. Have volunteers take turns with different approaches; then contrast them with the more constructive methods

Working It Out

15.2 Role-Playing the Customer

This exercise is good for developing tact in dealing with customer problems. Classes have already used this with real success. It fails only when students don't thoroughly understand the situation, or don't really understand role-playing as a concept.

Tips for Ron or Rhonda: This role-player needs to remember that he or she doesn't want to offend this customer, but refusing credit while retaining goodwill is going to be difficult. This player also needs to keep in mind that the company wants Mr. Wiggins to remain a cash customer in the future.

Tips for Delmar or Diane: Act innocent, as though you didn't have any idea your credit is less than ideal. Many slow payers act this way, so this is realistic. You should be willing to comply, but your attitude doesn't need to be a happy one. Act the way you would act if you were refused credit when you thought your credit was golden.

Case Study

15.1 Disaster in Aisle Three

1. What should Carmine say to Mrs. Raye? Why?

Student responses will vary. Probably the best course of action would be to speak to her in a normal voice and tell her that you're sorry that she had such an accident, making her understand that it was an accident and nobody is to blame, including your store. This is necessary, lest she

should later decide to sue the store. If you empathize with Mrs. Raye, it's easy to see why she is shouting accusations: she is embarrassed and likely a bit frightened. Whatever you can say to lessen the impact of both of those emotions will help.

2. What should he do, and in what order?

Carmine should immediately get all customers away from the area to prevent shards of broken glass from penetrating any of them. Both the safety of the customers and the treatment of Mrs. Raye are of utmost importance. Then, he should get a clean-up crew on the scene immediately; the faster the better, because the more fuss made about this accident, the more negative impact on customers. Mrs. Raye should be given a clean cart and helped to reshop for groceries she had already put in the old one. (You will assume that pieces of glass are in the cart and on the merchandise in the cart.) While an employee helps Mrs. Raye shop, he or she should calm her down as much as possible without emphasizing that the incident was the store's fault.

3. What should Carmine say to other customers who ask questions, such as: "What happened over there, anyway?"

You will get varied student responses here, too. The simple reply, "We had a little accident with one of our displays," should suffice. The main principle is that the curious customers should be answered, but without giving the incident undue emphasis. In no case should Carmine say, "It's really none of your business," or ignore the questioner.

Case Study

15.2 The Furniture Store Dilemma

1. What specific actions could Jasper Furniture have taken to prevent losing a long-term customer like the Caseys?

Some students might see the Caseys as not understanding the problems that retail outlets often have with suppliers. However, those who make that point are missing the one that this case is attempting to make. Even if you assume that the supplier really was totally responsible for the lateness of the shipment, the people at Jasper Furniture are still culpable and the Caseys have a right to expect more. If the Jasper people had called the Caseys regularly to update them on the lack of progress on the shipment, the Caseys' frustration would have decreased.

The furniture store is at fault not because of the late shipment as much as because of their treatment of the Caseys during that waiting period. They should have done all that was possible to find out the reason for the delay, then transfer that knowledge in a polite and timely manner to the customers. Causing the customer to feel even more ignored by the furniture store personnel has only compounded the problem. Mr. Casey is right when he says to them, "You could have salvaged the situation."

2. Pretend you are a new manager just hired by Jasper a few days before the final scene in the case. What steps would you take to restore the Casey's positive feelings about Jasper Furniture?

Answers will vary. Whatever answer the students give, though, should include some actions that could reverse the strong feelings of frustration and understandable anger that the Caseys already feel. One suggestion is to offer a percentage discount for the frustration the customers have already experienced. If the Caseys have prepaid, the refund should be sent with a letter of apology to the Casey home. Another suggestion is to promise the Caseys that you will find out exactly what's happening on the supplier end and that you will keep them apprised of the developing situation on at least a weekly basis—although it may be a too late for this. Creative students will come up with others.

3. List the principles in this chapter that this case illustrates.

The case illustrates several principles negatively:

1. First, customers want good feelings and solutions to problems. In this case, the feelings have not been taken into account, and the problems have not been solved.
2. The second of the "two simplest principles" of customer service has been violated. The furniture people have found out what their initial needs were, but did not follow up on doing whatever was necessary to fulfill those needs. In another sense, they also failed in identifying part of the need, which was reasonable promptness.
3. They have failed to establish a bond with these customers. These are longtime repeat customers; why hasn't a bond been formed with them and maintained throughout this ordeal?
4. The principle of "providing exceptional service" has been violated. This service has been exceptional only in the negative.
5. The principle of supporting the customer's self-esteem has also been violated. By virtually ignoring the Caseys and their needs, the Jasper people have done nothing to uphold and support their self-esteem. If anything, they have threatened it.

One could even make a case for seeing their treatment of the Caseys as unethical, especially if this was a full prepayment situation.

ADDITIONAL ACTIVITY

Customer Satisfaction Role-Play

This will involve students in simulated situations that will challenge their skills in dealing with customers and their problems.

Procedure: Choose a three-member role-playing troupe to play the customers. Try to get a cross-section of the class to represent a cross-section of potential customer types in the real world. Another small troupe of students should be chosen to play employees who are dealing with the customers. Give each group 15 minutes to rehearse in the hallway or in an empty room near the class. (If possible, give the employee troupe a couple of days to rehearse outside of class.) Have the students who play customers rehearse separately, or not at all, so the entire role-play will not be pre-planned. Reproduce the situations below and distribute to the class so that all members will understand the action taking place.

After each role-play, lead the class in a discussion of how each problem was handled, what was done well, and what could have been done more effectively.

Ask them to role-play the following situations:

1. "A Turkey Tale"
Characters:
Charlene (or Charles), a clerk in a health food store
Adam (or Arlene), a customer

Adam storms into the store carrying a 20-pound turkey. He claims to have bought the turkey the previous day. It is now the day before Thanksgiving. He is expressing a great deal of anger because he says, "The turkey is a strange color, is rotten, and smells bad." Charlene believes that there is probably nothing wrong with the turkey. The turkeys she keeps in stock have been raised entirely on organic vegetable matter and are treated hours before they are sold with a special herbal combination for extra taste and freshness. Most of her customers come to her store because of the high quality of her turkeys. She will agree that the turkey smells nothing like one from another store, but the smell is not "rotten," it is normal. It is pungent and pleasant, and the turkey will smell wonderful once it has been baked for a few hours.

2. "The Case of the Sticky Blazer"

Characters:

Josh (or Jane), the manager of the men's department at the Grande Bouche, a higher-end department store

Dr. Watters, an older man with a rather unpleasant face who is a customer in the men's department

Dr. Watters purchased an expensive navy blue wool blazer two days ago and is now coming in to the store to pick it up. As Josh helps him try on the blazer in front of the mirrors, Dr. Watters cries out in pain and quickly pulls the coat off. Apparently, the tailoring staff forgot to remove six straight pins from the lining of the coat after the alterations were completed. Dr. Watters is extremely upset, shouting epithets at Josh and cursing him for his incompetence. He claims he's bleeding and will have to see a doctor immediately. He even threatens to sue Josh and the store. Josh knows that this type of mistake rarely happens, though it has happened one other time in his two-year stint with the Grande Bouche. That customer had been more reasonable, he remembers. He needs to try to calm his irate customer, Dr. Watters, and keep him as the regular customer he has been for many years. Josh tries to summon all his skills to deal with this problem.

3. "The Aborted Trip"

Characters:

Lucy, the manager of a small travel agency

Mrs. Bellows, a customer

Mrs. Bellows usually plans her trips out of the country well in advance, but this year she waited too long. On Monday, just before closing time, she called her travel agent Lucy to ask for a booking on a package tour to Belize for the next Saturday. Mrs. Bellows knew this was short notice, but she thought that because she was a regular customer, Lucy would give her special treatment.

Today is Tuesday. After hours of research trying different angles on both the telephone and the Internet, Lucy has discovered that all tour packages to Belize have been booked, with a hefty standby list in every case. Now, Lucy has to give Mrs. Bellows the bad news, with the intent of keeping Mrs. Bellows as a regular customer. Ask students to role-play Lucy's character as skillfully as possible, remembering the principles learned in this chapter.

Managing Diversity

Chapter 16

LECTURE OUTLINE

I. A Diverse Society

A. There are many changes occuring in the composition of the American labor force as the U.S. enters the 21st century.
1. Women's labor force activity is increasing.
2. Older people are remaining in, or returning to, the workforce.
3. Immigration is resulting in a larger share of foreign-born employees in the U.S.
4. Non-Caucasian Americans are entering the workforce at a faster rate than Caucasians.
5. The marketplace is increasingly international.
6. White non-Hispanic males (the "traditional" employee) will make up only about 37 percent of the workforce by the year 2008.
7. Employees with disabilities and those with diverse religious beliefs will increasingly enter the workforce.

B. The changing composition of the workforce requires that everyone's knowledge and attitudes change with it.

II. Prejudiced Attitudes. All attitudes have three components: what you think, feel, and do. These three components are called cognition (thinking), the affect (emotions), and behavior. Attitudes or prejudice have their own names as follows:

A. **Stereotypes** are thoughts (cognitions) or beliefs about people or groups.

B. **Prejudice** is a bias in emotions or feelings about people or members of a particular group. Prejudice causes **bias**—a tendency to judge people before you know them, basing judgment on membership in some group or category of people.

C. **Discrimination** is the behavior, or what people do for, or against, a person or group because of their beliefs and feelings.
1. **Institutional racism** and **sexism** can result in discriminatory policies, with no feelings of bias in the policymaking.
2. The Civil Rights Act of 1964 (amended in 1972) makes it illegal to discriminate on the basis of race, color, religion, sex, or national origin. **The Equal Employment Opportunity Commission (EEOC)** monitors these laws.

III. Origins of Prejudice

A. Social causes of prejudice:
1. Prejudice allows people to feel superior by thinking of others as inferior.
2. Prejudice allows people to define themselves and feel socially accepted as part of their group.
3. Whether it is intentional or not, institutional support systems may create institutionalized discrimination.

B. Cognitive causes of prejudice:
1. **Cognitive categorization** makes your thought processes more efficient.
2. When you add value judgments to the categories, however, you create prejudice.

C. Emotional causes of prejudice:
1. **Ethnocentrism** is the belief that your group does things right, while others who do things differently are wrong.
2. Frustration can occur when you are competing for scarce resources. In this type of frustration, you may aggress against a target you perceive as taking (or threatening to take) your resources.

IV. Types of Discrimination

A. **Racism** is discrimination against someone based on their membership in a racial or ethnic group.

B. **Economic prejudice** is discrimination between the "haves" versus the "have-nots." (Note: This is sometimes called "classism," although this text does not use that term.)

C. **Sexism** is prejudice based on someone's gender.

V. Targets of Discrimination. In addition to those listed above, the following groups also encounter discrimination:

  A. Overweight people may have a difficult time being hired when an employer's values against obesity are turned into judgments of character flaws against them, or they are assumed to be a health risk to the company.

  B. Homosexuals may encounter homophobia, which is a very emotional, controversial, and long-standing type of prejudice. There are some laws that protect members of this group.

  C. Elderly people are often targets of prejudice (this is called **ageism**), but it is illegal to discriminate against people because of their age.

  D. People with disabilities may find employers reluctant to hire them out of fear they will be poor employees, although the opposite is usually true.

  E. Religious groups: Employers are not allowed to discriminate against employees because of their religious preferences, but there is disagreement about how to interpret the specifics of such laws.

  F. Pregnant women: Employers cannot base hiring, promotions, and firing on a woman's pregnancy.

VI. Sexual Harassment

  A. Sexual harassment is typically defined as unwanted sexual acts and requests, and creating a hostile environment.

  B. The Equal Employment Opportunity Commission (EEOC) reports that sexual harassment reports are on the increase. Most are filed by women, but about 10 percent are filed by men.

VII. Prejudice, Discrimination, and Self-Esteem

  A. Prejudice is often a sign of low self-esteem: The need to feel that others are inferior is used to boost one's beliefs about being superior.

  B. Prejudice can become a **self-fulfilling prophecy**, when victims begin to believe repeated messages that they are inferior, then act accordingly.

VIII. Looking Ahead. Some negative feelings and behaviors can be permanently eliminated, but there is no simple cure.

  A. Proximity (physical closeness) and contact can increase your understanding of people and groups who are different from you.

  B. Equal status between members of different groups encourages the belief that "they" are not inferior and "we" are not superior.

  C. Interdependence is when two groups or people must rely on each other in order to complete a task; this can be set up as a strategy for reducing prejudice between groups.

16.1 Assess Your Knowledge

  1. A true–false test for employees that evaluates their understanding of sexual harassment.

  2. A true–false test for management personnel that evaluates their understanding of their responsibility in stopping or preventing sexual harassment.

16.2 Reducing Sexual Harassment

  1. Write a policy statement.

  2. Post the policy statement in a public place.

  3. Talk about the policy.

ANSWERS TO IN-CHAPTER QUESTIONS

PHOTO, page 507: How can finding yourself in a new role or environment help you understand other people?

Answers will vary, but they should all be based around the fact that a new environment with diversity is an interesting, stimulating place where you can learn about and acquaint yourself with people who are different from you.

FIGURE 16.1, page 509: What changes do you see happening in your own field?

This depends on your field. For instance, if you are in engineering, you may notice that there are considerably more women in this field than there were even ten years ago. If you are in medicine, you may notice a steady increase in female doctors, even though pay disparities still exist between men and women in this field.

PHOTO, page 510: How can someone's prejudiced attitude affect others when he or she is working with the public?

Using prejudice while working with the public can lead to miscommunication, hostilities, and even violent interactions when people choose to misunderstand innocent intentions.

FIGURE 16.2, page 513: Which type of prejudice can be most damaging?

All types can be equally damaging because they can hurt people in serious ways, such as depriving them of employment or equal protection under the law.

PHOTO, page 515: How can you identify institutional prejudice?

Start looking for patterns—for instance, low hiring rates of women and minorities, or the excessive hiring of one group for a particular field or role—then ask yourself why. Often, the reason is institutional prejudice.

FIGURE 16.3, page 519: How can employers fight each of these?

Employers should always be on the lookout to prevent and eliminate institutional prejudice, and should strive to treat all employees and all positions as equally worthy of respect.

FIGURE 16.4, page 520: Why do these prejudices persist?

As with all prejudices, they persist because of bad habits, ignorance, and a fear of challenging one's own beliefs. In addition, many people still believe in the double standard that expects women to be passive and submissive, traits that are undesirable for anyone seeking success in the business world.

PHOTO, page 523: How can you deal with homophobia in the workplace?

Take any opportunity you can to counteract this prejudice as it arises. One thing you can do is "humanize" your homosexual coworker to anyone who is prejudiced. Most people will find it difficult to continue having prejudiced thoughts against someone after they learn that he or she is a hard worker, dedicated parent, or possesses admirable qualities.

FIGURE 16.5, page 526: How are people with disabilities better employees than most people think?

Statistically, people with disabilities have been shown to miss work less, change jobs less, and have great motivation to perform well at work. In addition, employees who are disabled can perform most jobs and fit in with any work environment.

FIGURE 16.6, page 529: What are the components of an effective sexual harassment policy?

The policy must be written concisely but in a way that covers all possible incidents and violations. In addition, it is not effective unless all employees are made to read and understand it.

FIGURE 16.7, page 531: Are any elements missing in any of these?

As you see at the bottom, these examples do not indicate if the behavior is welcome. If it is welcome, then it is technically not harassment. If, however, you are not sure if a behavior is welcome, it is best to avoid it.

Review Questions

1 **What are the three components of an attitude? What are the three components of prejudiced attitudes? Describe the three components of a prejudiced attitude.**

The three components of any attitude toward anything—whether an object, person, group, or situation—are what you think, feel, and do.

When you specifically talk about prejudiced attitudes, you can use these same three components: Here, the components become stereotypes, prejudice, and discrimination. Stereotypes are thoughts or beliefs about an object, person, or group. Prejudice is a feeling of pre-judgment and an evaluation of a person or a group before you know them. Discrimination is behavior toward the person or group. Discrimination can also include plans for action that you don't actually execute, or ways that you are inclined to act or would like to act but do not act out (known as behavioral intentions or inclinations).

2 **What individuals and groups can you think of who are likely targets of prejudice and discrimination? Do you fit into any of these groups that are likely targets? Have you ever found yourself a target of prejudice or discrimination as a member of this group? Explain.**

In this society, there are many different groups and individuals who are likely to be targets of prejudice and discrimination. For example, prejudice is directed toward people based on their ethnic group membership: African-Americans, Hispanic-Americans, Asian-Americans, and Native Americans are groups that historically have been targets of discrimination and prejudice. Prejudice based on race is called racism. Sometimes policies unintentionally create racism, as in the case of a state police policy requiring that officers be a minimum height, which unintentionally discriminates against most women, Asians, and many Hispanics. This type of prejudice is called institutional racism. Ethnocentrism, or seeing one's ethnic group as superior or somehow more correct, is in operation when people prejudge and negatively evaluate members of other ethnic groups.

Some people classify prejudice against Jews, or anti-Semitism, as a type of ethnic prejudice, but it is religious prejudice. Members of other religious groups often experience prejudice because of their beliefs.

Women belong to the largest group of people frequently targeted for prejudice and discrimination, even though they are not a numerical minority in this society. This type of prejudice is called sexism.

Individuals are also targets of prejudice and discrimination for many other reasons. Elderly people can be targets of prejudice and discrimination due to ageism—negative attitudes toward people based on their age. Overweight people are often targets of discrimination. Homosexuals are frequently targets of prejudice and discrimination—sometimes physically, as in the cases of "gay-bashing" where homosexuals are targeted for assault or murder because they are gay. Pregnant women have frequently been targets of discrimination in the workplace. Individuals with disabilities are also often targets of prejudice. Although there is not a strict class system in the United States, economic prejudice often exists between members of different socio-economic groups: "Haves" and "have-nots" often resent each other and may discriminate against each other on that basis.

Students' personal responses to experiences of discrimination will vary.

3 **Discuss some of the sources of prejudice. Within these sources, can you think of a particular prejudice that you have and how it arose? Explain your personal example.**

The three broad categories of sources of prejudice include social causes, cognitive causes, and emotional causes. These are discussed in detail below.

Social causes: One social theory is that feeling prejudice toward another person or group allows people to feel good about themselves by creating a feeling of superiority which raises their self-esteem (but artificially so, and at a cost to others). Another social theory is that prejudice helps people define themselves and feel socially accepted, such as when they belong to a group; but membership in the group (for example, a sorority or a sports team) means feeling loyal to the group above others, which can lead to prejudice. Another social cause is institutional support systems or policies, which unintentionally create prejudice.

Cognitive causes: These have to do with your thinking and reasoning processes. Part of efficient cognitive functioning is being able to quickly categorize objects, places, or people in a process called **cognitive categorization**. When you overgeneralize the categories and what they mean by assigning people to categories and then negatively evaluating them based on that category, this can become a cognitive cause of prejudice.

Emotional causes: Ethnocentrism is an emotional source of prejudice. This is the common human tendency to evaluate your own ethnic group as the most normal and correct; in other words, ethnocentrism is being "centered" around your own ethnic group. Another emotional cause is frustration when attaining a goal is blocked, especially when you are competing for scarce resources such as jobs or housing.

Students' responses will vary regarding the sources of their own prejudices.

4 Discuss the negative effects of discrimination in the workplace, both on the individual and on the business organization. Have you seen any discriminatory acts occurring in your workplace? Explain.

At the individual level, discrimination lowers the victim's self-esteem. According to psychologist Gordon Allport, discrimination can lead to self-blame, withdrawal from others, self-hatred, or aggression against one's own group; or blaming external causes and becoming suspicious of others, having increased pride in one's own group, or fighting back. The worst effect of discrimination at the individual level is the self-fulfilling prophecy, which is what happens when people start to believe the stereotype and the negative evaluation others hold for them, then become what the stereotype states about them.

At the organizational level, discrimination hurts the morale, productivity, and efficiency of the entire company. In the worst case, discrimination can hurt a company when it leads to legal action; lawsuits hurt a company's morale, profits, and public image.

Answers will vary as to students' experiences with discriminatory acts in their workplace.

5 Describe steps that can be taken in the workplace to reduce or prevent sexual harassment.

The **Equal Employment Opportunity Commission (EEOC)** has set guidelines for companies to follow regarding how to define sexual harassment. The EEOC also keeps track of sexual harassment complaints. They are a good resource for finding out what elements corporations can use in setting an effective policy. A typical policy statement would include a definition of what sexual harassment is—for example, "unwelcome sexual advances, requests for sexual favors, and other verbal or physical conduct of a sexual nature." Behaviors that would fit under this definition could include forced fondling, sexual slurs, unwelcome continued attempts at flirting, and suggestive pictures or materials in places where employees can see them.

Once it is written, the policy statement should be posted in a public place where all employees can see it. The company should also make a point of talking about the policy and stressing to employees how important it is that the policy is followed.

Sexual harassment is a big problem in this country, costing businesses and government entities millions of dollars a year in lawsuits, not to mention the damage done to the victims on an individual level.

6 How is institutional racism or institutional sexism different from open racism or sexism?

Unlike open and hostile racism or sexism, institutional racism or sexism is unintentional. It is the by-product of a business or government policy, and is not set up with the intent of discriminating against members of any group. This type of racism or sexism can be difficult to fight because it probably has a reason for being put into place that has nothing to do with racist or sexist outcomes, and administrators in the institution don't necessarily see that the outcome occurs as a result of the policy. Even when the intention is innocent, if the result is racism or sexism, then the original intent becomes irrelevant: It is still racist or sexist and will have to be changed.

7 What is meant by the term *self-fulfilling prophecy*? Think of an example in your own life or someone else's where a self-fulfilling prophecy (either positive or negative) arose. Explain your personal example.

A **self-fulfilling prophecy** is what happens when you tell a person (i.e., predict or prophesize, which explains where the name came from) that they are inferior in some way based on their belonging to some group, before knowing him or her as an individual. This is usually a group stereotype (such as ethnic or gender). After hearing this enough times, some people start to believe it and become what the stereotype (the prophecy or prediction) says they are.

A self-fulfilling prophecy can be positive or negative. For example, studies with school children show that when they are told they are above-average students, they often work up to the expectations placed on them. This can also work in a negative way, as when students are told they are below average and start to perform that way.

Students' examples will vary. In order to fit the definition of self-fulfilling prophecy, it has to be something the person became as a result of being told many times he or she would become that. The communication does not have to be one-on-one; it can be a cultural message coming from sources such as school, television, or books.

8 What are some of the common myths about people with disabilities in the workplace? What is being done to protect employment for this group?

The disabled are often seen as being unreliable, unable to do very many jobs, and discomforting to other employees. In fact, these are simply myths. Disabled employees have a lower average absentee rate than other employees, and they have a lower turnover rate in their jobs. There are also very few jobs today that disabled employees are unable to do, especially if some modifications to the job are made. Also, although some employees might be uncomfortable working with disabled coworkers at first, usually the discomfort is only temporary. Working with disabled coworkers can lead others to become less prejudiced toward the disabled as a group.

The disabled have been protected from job discrimination for over 25 years under the Rehabilitation Act of 1973. This law was difficult to interpret, though, because it did not clearly define "handicapped" or "disabled." In 1992 the Americans with Disabilities Act was enacted. The ADA prohibits discrimination by businesses in employment practices, as well as prohibiting discrimination in public transportation, telecommunication, and other privately owned public services (hotels, restaurants, bars, and so on). It also requires that benefits and opportunities for the disabled will be the same quality as those offered to others.

Critical Thinking Questions

9 **Under what circumstances is it acceptable to treat coworkers or employees differently because of their differences? Should you be blind to differences between coworkers or employees, or recognize them openly?**

Answers will vary. In many cases, such as with disabled employees, there must be a recognition and discussion of workplace modifications to allow successful employment.

Some students will say that a colorblind approach is the only equitable approach in treating people. If everyone is seen as the same, then there will be no discrimination. Others will say that this is an artificial approach since people cannot, even if they try, truly ignore the differences between themselves and others. In this view, to recognize differences openly and maintain an acceptance of these differences is more equitable in the long run.

10 **People today talk a lot about "tolerance." Is there a difference between *tolerance* and *acceptance* of differences, whether they be cultural, gender-related, religious, or other? Explain the differences.**

The word tolerance is a buzzword that has become overused in the past few years. Nevertheless, some students will not have heard it. This question can spark an interesting philosophical discussion about the difference between these two words.

Although it is meant in a positive light, "tolerance" implies a certain lack of acceptance ("I don't like broccoli, but I can tolerate it about once a month.") "Acceptance" conveys more of an attitude of recognition, celebration, and embracing differences between people. As Gene Roddenberry (creator of *Star Trek*) said, "Delight in diversity."

Working It Out

16.1 Impression Formation: Are Perceptions Influenced by Ethnicity?

This activity works best as an out-of-class homework assignment. This exercise has been assigned dozens of times, and the authors are always surprised (as are the students) at the willingness of many people to voice intensely prejudiced attitudes against identified groups. The first few times the authors assigned this activity, they expected that a climate of political correctness would prevent students from expressing openly hostile beliefs, but the anonymity of the situation apparently allows them to express beliefs openly.

The greatest value in this exercise is the discussion that arises afterward, when students are turning in their assignments. Students who are either high or low in prejudiced attitudes derive benefit from the discussion. "Student A," who is prejudiced and believes his or her group to be superior, now has the opportunity to hear reports from other students who have spoken about the inferiority of Student A's group. "Student B," who was disbelieving in class about the prevalence of prejudicial attitudes, now comes back to class after doing this assignment bewildered by, but more aware of, hateful beliefs that are so alien to him or her, and so hurtful to others.

Although there is a potential for controversy and conflict to arise from this assignment, the authors have never experienced any. Make certain that the responses collected by your students remain anonymous, and that in collecting the data, your students maintain an attitude of "objective reporters" who are simply collecting information, not challenging others' beliefs.

Be sure that you debrief students by reminding them that these beliefs may be common, but that does not mean they are true. Be sure to end with strategies for reducing stereotypic beliefs so that students don't leave with the idea that their stereotypic beliefs are valid and justifiable.

16.2 Gender Stereotypes in the Media

This exercise works best as an out-of-class activity, but you can bring in a stack of magazines or newspapers and conduct this activity in class.

Students typically find men portrayed in roles of authority, regardless of the product or information; for example, in advertising commercials (e.g., Are men really the "experts" on floor cleaners, dog food, or disposable diapers?), or in an advertising voice-over using a man's voice. Regarding television shows, men are portrayed more often in leading roles, and portrayed more often in the total number of roles (even though men and women both make up about half of the population). Women's roles are typically subordinate, and women or girls are portrayed less often in commercials or print ads.

Most students will find ads that demonstrate "faceism," or the tendency in ads to show men's faces more often, and women's faceless mid-sections more often. Women may be portrayed as less important, capable, and intelligent than men; or, similarly, as more innocent, less devious, and less capable of wrongdoing than men.

The greatest value in the exercise is seen in the discussions that arise when students turn the assignment in and discuss their results. Both men and women are usually surprised at the blatant sexism they find.

Because the media is a great socialization agent in this society, it transmits people's beliefs, attitudes, and values; it is very powerful.

■ INTERNET EXERCISES

Tips for Teachers

1. **Read and Summarize** As an alternate but related exercise, ask students to write about the different types of harassment that occur via the Internet (such as threatening e-mails, spamming, and viruses). Which seem to be the most common? The most serious? The most annoying?

2. **Compare and Contrast** Nolo.com offers a wealth of free legal advice for everything from small claims to wills and probate. As an additional exercise, ask students what they find regarding sexual harassment. Do they feel that existing legislation does enough to protect people from sexual harassment? Why or why not?

16.1 It's None of Your Business

1. Thinking about the questions, if you were considering hiring someone and wanted to be sure that you were hiring a reliable employee, these are things you might want to know as well. So, why can't you ask these questions? What is inherently wrong with wanting to know these things about a potential employee—why is it illegal?

At the most basic level, when you ask these questions of potential employees you reduce them to their socio-demographic characteristics, then make judgments about them based on these factors. Your decisions become based on your stereotypes, rather than on the person's qualities. For instance, if you decide not to hire a woman with young children because you assume she will be absent a lot due to her caretaking responsibilities, you are not giving her a chance to show you that she is a good employee regardless of her parental status. These stereotyped decisions deny the person the respect and acceptance they deserve.

2. Using the skills you have learned in previous chapters and the information you have learned in this chapter, what would you have said to this interviewer during the interview, in order to end these personal questions?

You could use the communication skills you learned in an earlier chapter to make assertive statements to the interviewer. You would need to make certain the interviewer knew that this line of questioning was illegal and you would not tolerate it. If a conflict then ensued between you and the interviewer, you could use the information you learned on conflict resolution to resolve it.

3. Let's say the interviewer continued this line of personal questions, even after you said something. The interview ended, and you were not hired. Would you have taken further action? Explain.

Because the Civil Rights Act of 1964 prohibits discrimination in hiring, you could take further action. You could begin by going through the university's human resources department. If you were not satisfied with their answer, you could file a complaint with the EEOC.

16.2 Two Against One

1. What type of prejudice is being illustrated here? What is it based on?

This sounds like prejudice from the "have-nots" against someone they perceive as a "have." This is a type of economic prejudice. The origins may be social ("I am not wealthy and do not belong with wealthy people; they are not like me and they make me feel uncomfortable."), emotional ("People who have less money prioritize their spending in the right way and focus on relationships, but wealthy people spend money foolishly and do not know how to behave around others."), or cognitive ("That person is wealthy. Wealthy people are always arrogant, greedy, materialistic, and selfish.").

2. If Elena did decide to fire Miranda in order to keep the peace within the department, what legal recourse would Miranda have, if any? Explain.

Miranda could certainly ask for an explanation for being fired without cause. She could take her complaint to the human resources department and file a complaint against Elena. If she was not pleased with the outcome, she could then decide if she wants to file a case through the EEOC, but since "haves" are not a protected class of people in any legislative acts, it would be difficult for her to support a discrimination case. However, she could still file a lawsuit for wrongful termination.

3. Let's say you have been called in as a mediator to settle this inter-departmental conflict. What steps will you take? What will these steps be based on?

A mediator would first have to find out what the problem is. Julia and Kathy don't really have grounds for their conflict with Miranda, and they may not want to admit prejudice based on envy. Miranda doesn't seem to have a problem with them; it sounds like the prejudice is one-sided.

The best way to reduce prejudice is to ensure that the people involved have contact with equal status and are interdependent. In this case, however, the best strategy might be for Elena to go through the conflict resolution suggestions in Chapter 13.

ADDITIONAL ACTIVITY

What Factors Contribute to a Feeling of Depersonalization?

This exercise will help students understand the effects of depersonalization on self-understanding and self-esteem. Most people have gone through being processed by some big, impersonal institution such as a hospital, school, service agency, or military unit. During such an experience, you may have felt like an object rather than a person. This process is called *depersonalization*.

Instruct your students to think about one of their own depersonalizing institutional experiences. Have them identify as concretely as possible what caused this feeling to take place. This exercise can be conducted in class in small groups, in class individually, or as a homework assignment. Have students answer the following questions:

1. What has been the most depersonalizing experience in your life? Why was it the worst?

2. Where did this depersonalizing experience occur? Briefly describe the place.

3. How did physical aspects of the institution contribute to your depersonalization? Were there impersonal-looking buildings or corridors, impersonal and characterless furniture, and so on?

4. How did processes that you encountered contribute to your feelings of depersonalization? (For example, were there stiff rules, long waits in line, procedures that failed to involve your name—or, if so, only your last name—and so on?)

5. What about the way people interacted—or failed to interact? Were there characteristics of the behavior of the other people you encountered that compounded the feeling of depersonalization?

6. If you had control of the institution you encountered, what specific changes would you make that would prevent others from undergoing an experience like yours?

Business Ethics and Social Responsibility

Chapter 17

LECTURE OUTLINE

I. What Is Ethics?

A. **Ethics** refers to the standards of conduct and morals in a society, based on the past and carried into the present.

B. **Morality** refers to how behavior should conform with cultural ideals of right and wrong.

C. There are several misconceptions about ethics and business held by the public:
   1. Business and ethics don't mix.
   2. Ethical dilemmas will have an obvious right or wrong answer.
   3. Ethics is simply complying with rules or regulations.

D. Ethics have no "teeth," but laws do.

E. A current, growing ethical controversy in business surrounds employees' rights to privacy on the Internet versus employers' rights to know how the time and equipment they have paid for are being used.

II. Codes of Ethics

A. **Ethical codes** are philosophical and procedural statements about ethics that are held by members of an organization.

B. Two companies that have exemplary codes of ethics are Johnson & Johnson and Texas Instruments.

C. Codes of ethics are usually based on one or more principles which include:
   1. The **principle of justice** (consistent and unbiased decisions, based on fact).
   2. The **principle of individual rights** (human rights and dignity).
   3. The **principle of utilitarianism** (achieving good for the most people).
   4. The **principle of individualism** (to achieve long-term self-interests).
   5. The **categorical imperative** ("What would it be like if everyone did this?").

III. Rationalizing Unethical Behavior

A. **Rationalizing** is finding reasons or excuses for your actions to reduce feelings of guilt. In this case, your guilt would arise because you know your behavior was unethical.

B. There are many beliefs that lead to rationalizing unethical behavior: for example, that nobody will notice, that the company would support it, and that the behavior is probably ethical and legal (without actually verifying this first).

C. People with high self-esteem are usually more likely to feel a healthy connection with those around them, and are more likely to act in a socially responsible way.

IV. Ethics in Context

A. Some employees engage in **boss massaging**, or expressing yourself dishonestly in order to gain and retain favor with your boss.

B. Boss massaging is often accompanied by undercutting coworkers. It should be discouraged.

V. The Influence of Group Goals

A. A company's ethical code can contradict your own ethical standards.

B. If you find you are making too many compromises, check your company's ethics to make sure you have interpreted them correctly; but don't wind up opposing your own values in order to keep your job.

VI. Global Ethics Issues

A. Ethical standards will vary around the world. Remember that *different* does not mean *deficient*. This idea will continue to gain in importance as global trade increases.

B. Historically, values and customs of other countries have different origins, evolutions, and applications. They are based on differing histories and cultural memories.

C. Examples of ethical practices that differ from those of the U.S.:

    1. **The inner circle:** A strong distinction is made between insiders and outsiders; outsiders are not as accepted.

    2. **Future favors:** Favors are traded back and forth, even across generations.

    3. **Gift exchange:** What seems like bribery to Americans is an expected exchange of gifts in many cultures.

VII. Social Responsibility

  A. Social responsibility is ethical behavior that demonstrates an understanding that everyone is part of a larger global community.

  B. There are many viewpoints about social responsibility, based on what group you believe you are responsible to.

    1. Traditional social responsibility holds that a company is responsible to itself and to making profits for its shareholders.

    2. Stakeholder social responsibility believes that a company is responsible to **stakeholders**—all groups a business interacts with (shareholders, customers, unions, suppliers, and so on).

    3. Affirmative social responsibility states that a company is responsible to all groups it interacts with, and also to society at large.

  C. There are many gray areas and difficult choices in social responsibility.

    1. A company that has been helping an organization may have to curtail that help, leaving the organization without funds.

    2. Choosing an organization to help means leaving other organizations without help.

    3. Motives for helping may be misunderstood within the community.

VIII. Blowing the Whistle

  A. Whistleblowing means turning in a person or company involved in unethical behavior.

  B. Whistleblowing is protected by law from retaliation, but most employees are still reluctant to blow the whistle.

  C. Ethical leadership makes whistleblowing unnecessary.

 17.1 Making Ethical Decisions: A Quick Ethics Test From Texas Instruments

  1. Is it legal?

  2. Is it consistent with the company's stated values?

  3. If you do it, will you feel bad?

  4. How would it look in the newspapers?

  5. Do you think it's wrong?

  6. If you're not sure, ask.

  7. If you don't get a clear answer, keep asking until you do.

 17.2 Becoming Culturally Aware of Ethical Conduct

  1. Look closely at the situation: Understand the other culture.

  2. Evaluate the intentions: Ask yourself what principles the ethical conduct is being based on, and whether your behavior would violate your own ethics or your company's ethics.

  3. Explore your options: If you have options, which are the most ethical?

ANSWERS TO IN-CHAPTER QUESTIONS

PHOTO, page 549: What are Bonnie's options now? What would you do if you were in her place?

Answers will vary. She could lodge a formal complaint with the company's human resources department, government agencies, or even take legal action, depending upon the strength of her evidence.

FIGURE 17.1, page 552: Do your personal ethics stay the same at your job, or do they change somewhat?

Many people's ethical standards change at least slightly to conform with their workplace's expectations. This can result in lowered ethical standards, such as when employees lie to preserve a company's or product's reputation; or they can result in higher standards, if a previously unethical employee finds himself or herself held to strict accountability.

FIGURE 17.2, page 554: Do you feel that this code is complete, or that more could be added?

Many people will feel that this ethical code contains everything that is necessary for a successful and ethical business, but you may discover other issues that need to be added.

PHOTO, page 556: How have you responded to pressures to behave unethically on the job?

If the pressure comes from within, you have to reassess your ethical standards, then get into the habit of remembering them at work when you are tempted to act unethically. If the pressure comes from your employer, you have several options, such as discussing the expectations with your employer to make sure you understand them correctly, going to human resources, or complaining to your local union.

FIGURE 17.3, page 557: What is your definition of the word "ethical"?

Any answer is acceptable as long as it reflects doing what you feel is morally right and considerate of others.

PHOTO, page 561: What do you do when a new cultural situation makes you uncomfortable?

If a new situation ever makes you uncomfortable, you need to ask yourself if this is from your own prejudices or expectations, or if it is from a genuine ethical conflict. If it is due to your own issues, you need to be more flexible; if it is a genuine ethical conflict, talk to fellow foreigners and others that you trust before making a decision.

FIGURE 17.4, page 562: Which of these propositions do you agree with most?

Students' answers will depend on their cultures.

PHOTO, page 564: How can you determine whether a situation is truly unethical, or if it is just your personal discomfort with the issue?

Look closely at the situation, examine the intentions, and then explore your options.

FIGURE 17.5, page 566: What is your favorite example of social responsibility? (It doesn't have to be from this list.)

Answers will depend on whatever cause means most to the individual. Human rights, environmentalism, helping needy or abused children, and scholarships are just a few popular causes.

PHOTO, page 569: What are the possible costs of not blowing the whistle on unethical corporate behavior?

The possible costs can range from unethical treatment of employees and customers to the loss of human lives.

Review Questions

1 **Briefly define *ethics*. Give your own definition of ethics as the term applies to your own values. Do you think it is a good idea to base your decisions on what "feels" right? Are there any outside forces that influence your behavior?**

Students will respond in a variety of ways, but answers to this question should stay within definitional parameters. **Ethics** deals with the standards of conduct and morals in a particular society that are based on the past and respected in the present. Students will likely use one or more of the possible answers from the ethics test provided in the text, or from the text itself. These include:

- What most people around them consider appropriate behavior.
- Whatever does the most good for the greatest number of people.
- Whatever action reflects the "Golden Rule."
- Whatever is not against the law.
- What their feelings tell them to do.
- Whatever action is in line with their religious beliefs.
- Whatever is customary in the society they are in.
- Whatever action would be approved of by a neutral panel of people in their line of work.

Of the suggested responses above, "What their feelings tell them to do" is a very popular choice. If you are using this question in class discussion, ask students who choose this definition to elaborate on "feelings." By that term, do they understand feelings to be "conscience" or just emotions? Are their feelings based on religious teachings? Societal norms? If so, are those ethical decisions really just feelings-based, and are feelings-based decisions necessarily ethical? Several other of these choices can be also examined for a thought-provoking discussion.

2 **What is a code of ethics? In your opinion, how effective are such codes?**

A code of ethics is an ethical philosophy and procedure statement that is accepted by all members of an organization.

In the opinion part of the question, student responses will vary. A very good answer would be that an ethical code is only as good as the people who follow it, and only as good as their level of commitment to follow it completely through, even when it might be painful or inconvenient to do so. In this way, Johnson & Johnson stands up well, for they are often used as an example of ethical and socially responsible actions (for

example, in the Tylenol incident several years ago) as well as words. The same can be said for Texas Instruments, which has won awards from business organizations for its code of ethics.

If this is a written response, you should expect at least some mention of the following approaches which include:

- The **principle of justice**: All decisions should be consistent, unbiased, and based on fact.
- The **principle of individual freedom**: Approach should be based on basic human rights and the dignity of the individual.
- The **principle of utilitarianism**: Decisions should promise to do the greatest good for the largest number of people.
- The **principle of individualism**: A person's primary goal is to achieve long-term self interest.
- The **categorical imperative**: Conduct should be based on a question, such as "What would the world, or my company, be like if everyone were to do this?"

3 **Evaluate the Johnson & Johnson Company's Code of Ethics on page 554. What is the key to its popular appeal?**

The Johnson & Johnson code is one of the best-written ethical codes in existence. It is a statement of the Johnson & Johnson philosophy, based on levels of responsibility they feel they have to specific constituents. Remembering Chapter 15, "Customers and Your Company Image," notice that the first responsibility is to all of their customer groups. One of the keys to its appeal is mentioned in question #2, above: The company follows through with actions and has proven so in several instances known to the public. The other appeal is the descending order of responsibility. Several other companies have adopted Johnson & Johnson's format.

4 **Define the term rationalizing. What role does rationalization play in making bad ethical decisions? Thinking back, have you ever rationalized a bad ethical decision? Explain.**

Rationalizing is thinking of reasons to excuse your unethical behavior. Some common rationalizations include thinking that the behavior is ethical and legal without actually finding out (because it is convenient and comfortable to believe this), believing that the company would expect the unethical behavior because it works in the best interest of the individual or the company, believing that nobody will notice, and believing that the company will go along with the behavior and protect the person because the company would have something to gain by the behavior.

If they are honest, most students will say they have used these or other rationalizations in making unethical decisions. These behaviors might be related to family life (I pinched my little sister because I thought nobody would notice) or social life (I walked out of the restaurant without paying my bill, but now I have more money for lunch tomorrow), in addition to unethical behavior on the job (I stole pens from the office, but my employer won't mind because the pens will make me a better person in the long run), or school (I cheated on my last Human Relations exam, but since the instructor didn't notice, all is well).

5 Explain the ethical problems involved in boss massaging. When is this practice a good idea? When is this practice a bad idea? Explain what may occur when employees are involved in boss massaging.

Boss massaging may be a good idea in the sense that it allows you to protect your job. However, in the long run, it is being dishonest with yourself and perhaps your values, so it is not helpful. Some employees are so invested in boss massaging that they do so at the expense of their relationships with coworkers: They engage in unhealthy competition with others at work, even undercutting them.

6 What major ethical issues are likely to confront someone who is doing business in a foreign country? Give some specific examples. What are some strategies for becoming culturally aware of ethical conduct in foreign countries?

Ethical standards will vary around the world. Remember that *different* does not mean *deficient*. This idea will continue to gain importance as global trade increases. Examples of ethical practices that differ from American practices are: the **inner circle**, in which a strong distinction is made between insiders and outsiders; **future favors**, when favors are traded back and forth, even across generations; and **gift exchange**, when what seems like bribery to Americans is an expected exchange of gifts in many cultures.

Strategies for becoming culturally aware of ethical conduct include looking closely at the situation to understand the other culture, evaluating the intentions by analyzing the basis for the principles behind the conduct, and asking whether your behavior would violate your own ethics or your company's ethics.

You should also explore your options in an ethics dilemma: If you have options, which are the most ethical?

7 How does the Internet create new ethical issues? Do you believe it is unethical for an employee to use the Internet on a company computer for personal use during company time? Is it unethical for the employer to monitor that usage? Explain.

The Internet has introduced gray areas of ethical behavior, related mostly to privacy. Who has access to an employee's browsing, and for what purpose? Other ethical issues include copyright violations, spreading viruses, selling and/or stealing addresses, and circumventing state or federal laws and taxes by selling products and services online. More issues will arise as the technology grows and changes.

Student responses will vary as to who is behaving unethically: Is it the employee who is "stealing" company time and equipment use for personal reasons, or employers who are "snooping" in an effort to monitor and control that usage? Regardless of their individual answers, students should demonstrate an understanding of both sides of this issue.

8 What is your attitude toward whistleblowing? Would you ever be a whistleblower if the situation merited such action? Why or why not?

Students' responses regarding their willingness to blow the whistle will vary. Students who are unwilling to do so may cite fear of retaliation, fear of embarrassment in case they are wrong, reluctance to be labeled a tattler, or fear for their professional future if they are known as a whistleblower. Those who say they would blow the whistle are most likely to cite the enormous importance in stopping the unethical behavior (while upholding their ethical and moral values) as a factor that outweighs any objections to blowing the whistle.

Critical Thinking Questions

9 There are times when people feel they must act unethically in the short term in order to benefit the greater good in the long term. Can you think of a time or a situation that you are familiar with in which this has happened? Is it *ever* acceptable to act unethically?

Answers will vary. Students typically will respond that unethical behavior is acceptable if it saves lives or accomplishes some noble deed in the long run.

10 Ethical standards often are made into laws over time. In Oregon, children under age 16 must wear helmets when riding bicycles. Several years ago, this was only an ethical standard that some parents chose and others did not. Do you think that all ethical standards should have "teeth" in the way that laws do? Who would govern codes of ethics? Or should some or all codes of ethics be made into laws so that they carry more weight?

Answers will vary. Some students will say that the differences between ethical standards and laws by definition mean that these should be separate, and only laws should have teeth. Others will say that some organizations have already put codes of ethics into place with teeth (e.g., the American Bar Association, and the American Medical Association) and that other organizations should model these practices by putting ethics violations into a stricter category. Still other students will say that because cultural beliefs vary so much around the world and even in the U.S., it would be impossible for anyone to govern or police ethical violations.

Working It Out

17.1 Ethical or Not?

This is a brief exercise that you can use at the very beginning of this unit to help students get a clearer focus of their own definitions of—and attitudes toward—ethics in business. Be sure that students understand each category before voting.

Working It Out

17.2 The Parable of the Sadhu

The lesson of this parable is the pressure of group goals versus individual responsibility. The group goal was to reach the 18,000-foot mountain pass and get to the village on the other side. A great deal of rationalization made the attainment of this collective goal defensible against all odds, including moral responsibility to a stranger. The basic question involves sorting out the tradeoff between individual moral responsibility and individual responsibility to help attain the goals of one's group. Students often point out that the danger sign is when an individual has trouble answering the question, "Would I act in this manner if I were all alone, and not the member of this group or company?" (Incidentally, some students may think that Bowen McCoy is a terrible person; others often contend that he is better than his behavior suggests because he has cared enough to admit his wrong publicly; and still others see his writing the article as a kind of penance.)

The opinion part of the question is, of course, specific and personal. However, any workplace could be improved by sorting out group and individual goals and by becoming more articulate about right and wrong choices in the process. Employees and managers both should get accustomed to asking, "Would I act in this manner if I were all alone, and not the member of this group or company?"

The issue of prejudice and discrimination also gets mixed into a class discussion of this parable. Some students create a hypothetical alternate case wherein the sadhu was replaced by a white Caucasian male from a European country or the U.S. Would he more likely have been helped? It's an aside, but one that the instructor should be prepared for, and one that is quite relevant to Chapter 16.

■ INTERNET EXERCISES

Tips for Teachers

1. **Read and Write** A related subject is a bill of rights for Internet consumers. Overall, do you think that E-businesses act ethically enough? Why or why not? What should a bill of rights for Internet consumers do, and how should it be enforced?

2. **Read and Summarize** Ask students to write down new ideas for corporate volunteerism, then e-mail a letter to a company asking them to consider some kind of charitable giving for a specific cause. Follow up two weeks later to see who got responses and what those responses were.

17.1 Life Over Profit

1. Was the husband's behavior excusable under the circumstances?

Answers will vary. Some students will say that stealing is never acceptable under any circumstances, while most will say that it is acceptable in these circumstances.

2. If you were a police officer in the town, would you have arrested him for theft?

Answers will vary. Students often say that while most police officers would arrest him, they personally would not. Some students will say that upholding the "letter of the law" is the most important principle to follow, while others will say that morals and ethical standards come before the law and help define a law's true intent, or the "spirit of the law."

3. If you were Heinz, would you have stolen the drug? If not, why? What would you have done instead?

Answers will vary. Most students will say that they would have stolen the drug. Some students will insist that there must be other options, such as working out a payment plan for the drug, appealing to a higher authority, or letting nature take its course in his wife's illness.

Case Study

17.2 Boss Massaging, or Just Good Politics?

1. Do you think Josh is really doing anything wrong? Why or why not?

Josh is **boss massaging**, which in itself is being dishonest to one's own values in the interest of retaining favor with one's boss. Whenever someone gets hurt in the process of boss massaging, it is wrong. Josh is undercutting Denise, and that is damaging to their relationship and to the organization overall.

2. Why does Denise feel the way she does about Josh's behavior? Is this just a case of sour grapes on her part, or does she have a legitimate complaint? If she has a legitimate complaint, to whom should she voice it?

Denise feels betrayed and manipulated. She feels that Josh has put his aspirations ahead of their working relationship and the overall health of the company. If Josh is chosen for the promotion, his unethical behavior does not bode well for his future management style. This complaint will not be easy to voice to Jane Wu, for Denise's complaint may be seen by Jane as sour grapes. Also, Jane may not believe Denise because Jane's self-esteem would be damaged by hearing that Josh's friendship with her is insincere, based on nothing more than wanting a promotion that only she has the power to grant. Denise may be able to voice her concerns to the human relations director, but this will probably not change the outcome of the promotion; it may even hurt her in the long run to be seen as a tattler who goes over her supervisor's head with complaints.

3. What do you think will happen in this situation if it plays out to its logical conclusion? What do you see as the long-term consequences in terms of the relationship between Josh and Denise?

In the real world, Josh would probably get the promotion. The damage done to Josh's and Denise's working relationship is probably beyond repair. Josh may announce plans to "clean house" and replace Denise, or Denise may decide on her own to leave the company.

ADDITIONAL ACTIVITY

Corporate Secrets

This exercise will allow students to examine another dimension of corporate ethics that is not specifically addressed in the book, and allow for class discussion on this difficult topic.

Reproduce the case below and divide the class into groups of four or five for case discussion. Have each group report its conclusions via a spokesperson chosen for that purpose. The class can then arrive at a majority opinion based on the patterns of consensus from the different groups.

The Case: Faye Little was hired by a successful computer software company and was initially quite impressed with her new employer. The company seemed progressive, friendly, and not at all sexist. The new software they were producing was specifically targeted at the construction and large equipment manufacturing industry. Faye had a background in both mechanical and architectural engineering. Most of the software up to the time of this case had been supplied by companies in the United Kingdom. Faye had been working for a competitive firm in the U.K. just before coming back home to the U.S. She had begun missing her relatives and friends in this country, and was happy to be back.

Faye's new employer mentioned when she was first hired that her knowledge of industrial software would be a real plus. Faye had thought that he was referring to the broad base of experience the previous job had given her, but soon it became apparent that the employer had other things in mind. After just two weeks on the job, her boss John Attleton called her into his office and asked her to provide him with some of the software from his main competitor overseas—the very company Faye had just left. Attleton was so matter-of-fact in his request that Faye had to do a quick self-analysis. "Wait a minute," she thought to herself. "He is asking me to commit corporate espionage!" As she reflected, she recalled that her British managers had adamantly taken the position that theft of software ideas was as serious as theft of money. She had signed a notarized agreement never to tell corporate secrets.

"I can't do it," Faye said suddenly. "I feel that corporate espionage is unethical, and I won't have any part of it."

"But this is a foreign country we're talking about here. You know as well as I do how much of this country's economy those people already control, what with British Petroleum, Shell Oil, Pillsbury..."

"I'm sorry," answered Faye. "Wrong is wrong, whether it's another country or my own. I certainly hope this wasn't the reason you hired me, because if it is, I'm bound to be a big disappointment."

"Come on, Faye," said Attleton. "Everyone does it. It's no big deal. Our other employees would do the same thing in your place."

Faye stood firm. "Tell me right now whether I should be handing in my resignation."

Questions for Group Discussion

1. Would you have done the same thing if you had been in Faye Little's place? Why or why not?
2. Is there any ethical difference between the corporate theft of ideas and merely passing information? Explain.
3. Do you feel that Faye should "blow the whistle" at this point in her dealings with Attleton? Should she quit? What should she do?

Maintaining Workplace Health

LECTURE OUTLINE

I. Defining Personal Problems

  A. Employees who bring personal problems to work affect everyone in the workplace.

  B. Problems at work can arise when employees abuse alcohol or drugs, have problems with their marriage or family life, have financial problems, or are suffering from medical disorders.

  C. Problems in one area can lead to problems in other areas causing a chain reaction.

II. Employee Assistance Programs (EAPs) treat employees with life issues, such as alcohol and drug dependence, marriage and family conflicts, and financial difficulty.

  A. For EAPs to work, employers must be willing to watch for problems and confront employees if needed.

  B. EAPs can reduce a company's health care costs, absences, grievances, accidents, lost work hours, and disciplinary problems.

III. Substance Abuse: Alcohol and Drugs

IV. Alcohol Abuse

  A. Untreated alcohol and drug abuse cost U.S. businesses almost $200 billion dollars per year in lost productivity and health care costs.

  B. At least 95 percent of alcoholics and 70 percent of drug abusers work.

  C. Alcoholism cuts across all occupational, ethnic, racial, social class, and gender categories.

  D. There are many physical signs of alcohol abuse, such as slurred speech and bloodshot eyes.

  E. There are many behavioral signs of alcohol abuse in the workplace, including missing work often, being late or leaving early, irritability, conflicts with coworkers, blaming others, lowered job performance, and financial problems.

  F. There are several strategies employers can use to fight alcohol abuse.

    1. Develop a company policy against alcohol abuse.

    2. Put drug and alcohol abuse awareness campaigns into place.

    3. Train supervisors.

  G. Denial is a common characteristic of alcohol or drug abuse.

    1. Supervisors should not accuse employees directly of having an abuse problem.

    2. Make the employee understand that his or her job performance is not acceptable.

    3. Supervisors should not try to counsel or advise employees themselves.

V. Employee Drug Abuse and Dependency

  A. Substance abuse and substance **dependence** can arise from the use of any psychoactive drug, whether legal or illegal.

    1. Substance abuse is continued use of a psychoactive substance even after it is causing problems in a person's life.

    2. **Physiological dependence** includes **tolerance**, or needing more of the substance to get the desired effect, and **withdrawal symptoms** when drug use is stopped.

    3. **Psychological dependence** (or **preoccupation**) is craving a drug and organizing your life around getting and using it.

    4. A **psychoactive drug** is any substance that affects a person's judgment, behavior, mental processes, moods, conscious experience, or perceptions.

  B. Drugs can be categorized into four categories, depending on the type of effect they have on the **central nervous system** (the brain and spinal cord).

    1. Depressants

    2. Stimulants

    3. Narcotics

    4. Hallucinogens

VI. The Effects of Substance Abuse in the Workplace

  A. Substance abuse problems are expensive to the workplace and to the American economy.

  B. Symptoms of drug abuse affect other employees in terms of lowered morale, lost group productivity, and safety issues.

VII. Responses to Substance Abuse
   A. Employee drug testing
      1. The Drug-Free Workplace Act of 1988 states that businesses must take action to make the workplace drug-free.
      2. Employers must balance employees' privacy rights against business safety issues.

VIII. Substance Abuse Management Policies. These policies should be written by the company, then posted with counseling and referral information.
   A. Public employees have added responsibilities to maintain a drug-free workplace.
   B. Small businesses can use the services of the Department of Labor, the Small Business Administration, and the Office of National Drug Control Policy for help with substance abuse policy problems.
   C. The U.S. or local Chamber of Commerce can also provide information and services for the "Drugs Don't Work" program.

IX. Marital, Family, and Other Personal Problems
   A. Family problems can spill over into the workplace. These problems have their own distinct symptoms:
      1. Excessive tardiness or absences.
      2. Unusual behavior, such as crying or losing one's temper.
      3. A decline in work performance.
      4. Trouble concentrating.
      5. A decline or change in appearance.
   B. Divorce or marital conflict is very common and leads to added stress, time pressures, psychological problems, and financial problems.
   C. Domestic or **family violence** includes physical, verbal, emotional, or sexual abuse. This problem is very common (it affects an estimated one out of four women in the U.S.), and is also very expensive for businesses and the American economy.

X. Financial Problems
   A. Financial problems can arise as a result of other problems, such as substance abuse or divorce.
   B. Stress due to financial problems may cause other problems, such as substance abuse or marital difficulty.
   C. **Compulsive gambling** causes problems for the person with the gambling problem, coworkers, and families.
   D. EAPs and consumer credit counseling services can help employees with financial problems.

XI. Medical Disorders That Affect Mental Health
   A. Some medical disorders can cause symptoms that mimic substance abuse. As many as one in five employees has a type of this disorder, in a mild or more serious form. Examples of such disorders include:
      1. Depression: major clinical depression (unipolar), or bipolar depression.
      2. Anxiety disorders.

   B. These disorders can be successfully treated with medications, psychotherapy, or both, along with some accommodations from the employer. Employees should not try to self-diagnose, and employers should not serve as informal counselors.

XII. AIDS/HIV in the Workplace
   A. Acquired Immune Deficiency Syndrome (AIDS) is among the top five causes of death for adults aged 25–44.
   B. The Americans with Disabilities Act (or ADA; see Chapter 16) protects the rights of employees with AIDS or those who are infected with the human immunodeficiency virus (HIV).
   C. Managers of AIDS/HIV infected employees must create an atmosphere of acceptance for these employees, inform them of their health care rights and benefits, accommodate them in their illness, provide information on disease transmission and bereavement counseling to coworkers, and be willing to confront their own attitudes and values related to this disease.

18.1 Look for Warning Signs. Warning signals for substance abuse are similar to alcohol use. These signals can also appear:
   1. Difficulty in recalling and following instructions.
   2. Frequent lateness to work.
   3. Frequent absences or disappearances from job location.
   4. Taking too many cigarette or restroom breaks.
   5. Taking extended lunch and work breaks.
   6. Difficulty getting along with coworkers.
   7. Making an increasing number of mistakes on the job.
   8. Repeated accidents off the job that affect job performance.
   9. Dramatic changes in personality or work performance during the day, especially after taking a break.

18.2 Know When to Intervene
   1. Observe the employee to see how job performance has been affected.
   2. Provide opportunities for the employee to talk with you.
   3. Create an atmosphere of trust and concern for the employee.
   4. Encourage the employee to take action, such as getting counseling.
   5. Guide the employee toward developing a plan of action.
   6. Follow up with the employee.
   7. Allow time for the problem to be resolved. Keep communication lines open.

ANSWERS TO IN-CHAPTER QUESTIONS

PHOTO, page 585: Is Jared showing signs of alcoholism? What do you think DeAnna should do?

Jared is showing signs of alcoholism by neglecting his family responsibilities, breaking the promise to his wife that he will no longer continue this behavior, and coming home drunk every Friday night.

Answers will vary.

FIGURE 18.1, page 588: What kind of services do you think a company should offer?

Many people feel that all EAPs should offer free counseling and referrals, as well as information on drug and alcohol abuse. They also feel that counseling and referrals should be available for people experiencing family conflicts such as divorce or family violence, as well as for people with financial problems. In addition, many would like to see referrals for day care and elder care.

PHOTO, page 589: When should an employer intervene with an employee's suspected alcoholism?

Employers should intervene when they notice a change in the employee's work performance, and the emphasis should remain on the employee's work. If an employer notices a long-term problem that does not affect job performance but appears to be hurting the employee personally, the employer can intervene, but this must be handled very carefully to insure that the employee is not offended or files a lawsuit.

FIGURE 18.2, page 594: In your own words, what is the difference between substance abuse and dependence?

Substance abuse is the irresponsible use of any substance, to the point where it interferes with one's work or personal life. Dependence is when a person cannot live without a drug and has lost control over its influence in his or her life.

FIGURE 18.3, page 599: What are the most common side effects of drugs?

The most common ones are general irritability, depression, and mild illness. However, most of these drugs can also lead to psychosis and death.

PHOTO, page 602: How can employers develop substance abuse education that is informative and useful?

First, a company needs to develop a policy that is fair, accurate, and consistent through the entire organization. Next, employees need to be educated thoroughly on this policy and why it needs to exist. Finally, the company should emphasize that resources are available (such as an EAP) for employees who need help.

FIGURE 18.4, page 609: What can employers do to help an employee that has a gambling problem?

If an employee has gambling problems, he or she will also have financial problems; these can cause stress and lowered productivity, and also may make the employee susceptible to stealing from the company in some way. Employers should take action at the first signs of lowered work performance to ensure that the employee gets the help he or she needs.

FIGURE 18.5, page 610: What could you use a credit counselor for?

Answers will vary, depending on your needs. If you are a student, perhaps you want to help build up your credit without building up too much debt. If you find that you are using credit cards too much, perhaps you would like to learn alternatives to making ends meet. Perhaps you need to be redo your monthly budget. In any event, credit counselors have sound advice for everyone.

FIGURE 18.6, page 612: How should employers approach employees who appear to have mental health disorders?

Answers will vary, but it is always important to let the employee understand that your focus is on his or her work performance and that you are not judging the condition in any way.

PHOTO, page 613: What are different approaches that employees should take to combat a mental health disorder?

Many people make positive changes through medication and therapy; others find that changes in diet and lifestyle will reduce or eliminate a mental health disorder. Sometimes a combination of all four works best.

Review Questions

1 **What are the differences between substance abuse, physiological dependence, and psychological dependence?**

There is no clear line between substance use and substance abuse, but substance abuse can be rationalized by the user continuing to use a psychoactive substance, even when it is causing or worsening the problems in the person's life. These problems can affect the person socially, physically, and mentally. **Substance abuse** includes frequent, intense, and compulsive use of a drug, whether legal or illegal. It isn't the exact amount of the drug that makes it abuse, but the effects caused from its continued use.

Substance abuse is the first step to physiological and psychological dependence. **Physiological dependence** includes tolerance, which is needing more and more of a drug to feel the same desired effects, and experiencing physical withdrawal symptoms when the drug is not used. **Psychological dependence** or **preoccupation** is when the person craves the effects of the drug and organizes his or her life around getting the drug and using it. In other words, when a person has lost control over the drug, psychological dependence has occurred.

2 **What are some physical signs of employee alcoholism? What are some behavioral signs or warning signs of employee alcoholism?**

Warning signs of employee alcoholism include both physical and behavioral signs. Physical signs include changes in a person's appearance, slurred speech, bloodshot eyes, the smell of alcohol on the person's breath, and an unsteady walk. The person may have chemically-caused memory loss or "blackouts."

Behavioral signs include missing work often, being late to work or leaving early, taking frequent long lunch hours or breaks, personality changes such as irritability, avoiding or having conflicts with supervisors and coworkers, blaming other people when things go wrong, resenting supervisors or complaining of feeling picked on, lowered job performance or reduced efficiency, having financial problems including having wages garnished, and psychologically-caused memory repression or memory loss.

These are similar to the signs to look for in any substance abuse problem, not just alcoholism.

3 **Why is drug testing in the workplace controversial? What are the legal issues involved in drug testing? How can drug testing affect employee morale? What are the different ways companies can handle drug testing?**

The controversy over drug testing arises because there is a conflict between protecting Americans' Fourth Amendment rights to privacy against search and seizure activities, balanced against the rights of businesses and private citizens to be free from substance abuse at work.

The Drug-Free Workplace Act of 1988 says that certain businesses have to make their workplaces drug-free, and this may include drug testing. How drug testing is handled has a lot to do with employee morale. Although drug testing can prevent and detect drug abuse at work, it can also suggest to non-abusing employees that their employers do not trust them, or that their employers suspect them of substance abuse even though they are not substance abusers.

Companies handle drug testing in different ways and according to different schedules, such as randomly while the employee is working for them, or only when the employee is being hired. They also handle positive drug test results in different ways, from firing employees on the spot to retaining them and referring them to an EAP. If employers are not careful about testing and handling positive test results, they can leave themselves open to lawsuits because Title VII of the Civil Rights Act defines substance abuse recovery as a disability, and discriminating against the disabled is illegal.

4 **What are some suggestions for statements that should be included in company policies to combat alcohol and drug abuse at work?**

Drug and alcohol policies should be clearly communicated to everyone at work, with the same penalties for all levels of staff. Components that should be included are drug awareness education for employees and their families, health care, and counseling and referral for employees who need it. The policy should allow for honest and direct answers to employees' questions, and should focus on non-users, with personal issues such as health and safety being targeted. The policy should be clearly stated so that it is fair, accurate, and legal.

For small businesses that cannot afford counselors or other resources that larger companies can afford to provide, the Department of Labor and the Small Business Administration along with the Office of National Drug Control Policy can help with substance abuse policy problems. The U.S. or local Chamber of Commerce can also provide information and services for the "Drugs Don't Work" program.

⑤ What is meant by compulsive gambling? What is the relationship between gambling and other problem behaviors, such as substance abuse? What main factor separates compulsive gamblers from casual or occasional gamblers?

Compulsive gambling occurs when people are addicted to the need to make money—the thrill of gambling. Their need to gamble becomes as uncontrollable as any substance abuse. This is not a rare problem: estimates are that as many as 8–12 million people in the U.S. are compulsive gamblers.

One of the problems with compulsive gambling is that it can lead to other problems, such as marital or family problems, substance abuse problems, or possibly even criminal activity as people try to obtain money for gambling. They may be getting themselves deeply into debt in order to cover their gambling losses. They may also be suffering from depression.

The main factor that separates compulsive gamblers from casual or occasional gamblers is that compulsive gamblers are unable to control their behavior even when it is causing problems in their lives, just as anyone who has any other type of dependency is unable to control his or her behavior.

⑥ What are some warning signs that family violence may be occurring among employees? Why is family violence a problem in the workplace?

Some warning signs that may be signaling **family violence** include absenteeism, unexplainable injuries, conflict with coworkers, or the employee being preoccupied and upset at work. Abuse in a family can be physical, emotional, verbal, and sexual. This is another expensive type of family problem, costing American businesses billions of dollars per year in absenteeism, lost productivity, and abuse-related medical costs.

When a person is involved in family violence, it most likely shows up in a weakened work performance. An employee who is the victim of abuse may be too ashamed or embarrassed to talk about it at work, which makes it harder to give referrals or get the employee into counseling. If the employee is the abuser, he or she may also be ashamed or embarrassed, but also possibly afraid of prosecution or other legal action, so it will be difficult to refer this employee also.

Family abuse and domestic violence often include substance abuse as well, which adds another layer of problems to the workplace.

The abuse victim's coworkers can also suffer when they fear that the violence may spill over into incidents at work. Coworkers may also be distressed by trying to help the victim. Employers may feel that because the abuse is a family problem, it is too personal to talk about, and so they should not intervene.

Family or domestic violence is an all-too-common occurrence, with estimates that one in four women will be a victim of domestic violence at some time in her life.

⑦ What are the differences that distinguish anxiety, depression, and bipolar disorder? Why are these medical problems sometimes mistaken for substance abuse?

These disorders can all lead to absenteeism, fatigue at work, low work performance, inability to pay attention, and numerous other symptoms, but they are all very different disorders.

Anxiety disorders are the most common type of mental health problem, affecting about 30 percent of women and 19 percent of men at some time in their lives. Symptoms can include intense fear, worry, apprehension, reliving past traumas, phobia, panic attacks, obsessive-compulsive behavior, and disturbed sleep.

Depression is called the "common cold of mental disorders" because everyone experiences it at some time or another. Major depression can cause sadness, lack of interest in normal activities, loss of energy, and disturbed eating and sleeping patterns.

Bipolar disorder, which used to be called manic depression, is a type of depression. It includes alternating periods of depression and frenzied (or manic) activity.

These disorders can all be successfully treated with medications and psychotherapy. Employers may need to make some accommodations for employees with these disorders by allowing more flexible scheduling, reducing workplace distractions, and allowing other modifications that can help the employee maintain a high level of productivity.

⑧ What responsibilities do managers have to employees who are AIDS/HIV-infected and to employees who are not infected?

Managers must accommodate AIDS/HIV-affected employees in their jobs so that they can remain in these jobs for as long as they are willing and able to work. Managers should check to make sure that all the other company factors are in effect for the employee: For instance, the company's EAP can provide counseling if these employees are interested, and health care benefits will continue for these employees. Family and coworkers should expect the company to be ready with information on death and bereavement issues, as well as information on disease prevention. AIDS is a frightening disease, and managers will have to confront their own feelings and values before designing and instituting a policy to address this issue and protect the dignity of all employees involved.

Critical Thinking Questions

9 Read the *Time* magazine article "Mental Adjustment: How Far Should Employers Go to Help Someone with a Psychiatric Illness Stay on the Job?" (May 19, 1997, Vol. 149, No. 20). This article is also located on-line at:
> http://www.ime.com/time/magazine/1...m/970519/society.mental_adjust.html

What is *your* opinion about how far employers should go in order to accommodate employees with mental disorders?

Answers will vary. Since courts of law and organizations are unable to agree on how to settle this question, students will probably also be unable to agree. Most students will say that there is a point at which employers will have to draw the line in making accommodations for employees with mental illnesses, but they will disagree as to where that line should be drawn.

10 The public has a right to expect workplaces to be safe and free from drugs. At the same time, individuals also have a right to privacy. What's your view on how far employers should be able to go in drug testing of employees? What would you do if you suspected a coworker had a substance abuse problem?

Similar to the issue presented in the preceding question, this issue is far from settled. Most students will agree that they do not want to buy services or goods from (or work at) a place where employees are under the influence of a psychoactive substance, but they disagree on where the line should be drawn regarding drug testing. Interestingly, some students have responded that they use drugs, and would not agree to be tested at work, while others have responded that they use drugs, and would be willing to be tested at work as long as all others are being tested as well. Students' answers will vary.

Working It Out

18.1 Alcohol Dependency Self-Quiz

The purpose of this quiz is to let students take a serious look at their drinking behavior in a confidential and unthreatening way. From time to time, you may have students who want to discuss problem drinking with you, or want your help in treating themselves or someone close to them. It is not your responsibility to counsel them (unless you are a trained counselor, and you are willing to take on that responsibility). Instead, if they seem to be upset by their self-quiz results, you should be prepared to refer them to the student health center, a community mental health center, Alcoholics Anonymous, or some other outside resource.

Many students will not want to admit their alcohol dependence. Their response may be seen in their failure to take this quiz seriously. Many (especially younger) students still see drinking as an entry into an adult world, so they will not take it seriously, either. If you maintain a serious attitude and encourage anyone who thinks they may have a problem to contact their Employee Assistance Program (EAP) or any Alcoholics Anonymous (AA) group in their area for more information, you will at least be planting a seed for that thought.

Working It Out

18.2 Workplace Health

This exercise allows students to understand the typical behaviors associated with problem employees. Your job as the instructor will be to rotate around the room while the exercise is going on and make sure that students express the "symptoms" correctly, with the appropriate interventions.

INTERNET EXERCISES

Tips for Teachers

1. **Read and Summarize** To spark further discussion about substance abuse, you can ask the students some or all of the following questions:
   - Why do family members and close friends of substance abusers let the abuse continue? Is it their fault, or is it really out of their hands? What is the best thing someone can do to help?
   - Some people say that they do not label someone an alcoholic unless that person admits to their alcoholism. Considering the frequent use of denial in alcoholics, is this a wise choice?
   - Many people in organizations attend happy hours, and they generally feel that one to two beers per night doesn't make them alcoholics. Do you agree? Under what circumstance would they be incorrect?

2. **Read and Summarize** Ask students if they agree that every workplace needs to be drug-free. Why or why not? Which types of workplaces should *always* have high drug-free standards?

Case Study

18.1 Is It Catching?

1. From this description, do you agree that Brandon Lee has AIDS? If so, do Linda and Chantel have anything to worry about? Explain.

We can't know by looking at him, but it's certainly possible that Brandon has AIDS. Linda and Chantel do not have anything to worry about as far as being exposed to the virus just by casual contact with him.

2. What should the bank's EAP offer Brandon? His family? His coworkers, such as Linda and Chantel? How would you feel in Linda or Chantel's place?

Brandon can expect to be accommodated in his job so that he can remain in it for as long as he is willing and able to work. He can expect his company's EAP to provide counseling if he wants it. He can expect his health care benefits to continue. Brandon's family and coworkers should expect his employer to be ready with information on death and bereavement issues, as well as information on disease prevention. AIDS is a frightening disease; Linda and Chantel are probably fearful and will need that fear addressed by management.

3. What are Brandon's rights in this case? Do you expect that he will be fired, asked to resign, or demoted? Explain.

Brandon should expect to retain his job for as long as he is willing and able to work. The Americans with Disabilities Act (ADA) protects HIV and AIDS-infected employees.

Case Study

18.2 Absent on the Job

1. What is going on with Janelle? Do you agree with Amir that she is probably having personal family problems? Could anything else be going on here?

Janelle is most likely having family problems because she is upset and her work performance is declining. She says that she is preoccupied, but is reluctant to tell Amir what the problem is. It could be marital problems, financial problems, abuse or violence in the home, or even childcare problems. It is difficult to tell from the description exactly what is going on with Janelle, but it doesn't seem to fit the description of substance abuse or the other problems mentioned in this chapter.

2. What are Amir's responsibilities here? What should he do?

Amir is responsible for seeing that the agency runs smoothly. He has to see that Janelle gets whatever help she needs because she is losing productivity. She is also involving other people by making the secretary upset and taking Yvonne's attention away from her work. This is probably causing lowered productivity and morale all through the agency, because it is a small enough business that the other employees will have noticed something wrong with Janelle.

Amir's first responsibility is to follow through with his conversation he had with Janelle a few weeks ago. She said that everything would be straightened out, but it isn't. He should give her another opportunity to explain what is going on so that he can refer to her appropriate resources. If she doesn't want to tell him, he should still refer her because EAPs will keep her situation confidential. He also needs to make it very clear to her that her performance is not acceptable, and that he will take disciplinary action, if necessary. He should then follow up with such action if she does not seem to be improving. Amir also needs to make it clear to the other employees in the office that they are not responsible for Janelle's welfare, and that their productivity needs to return to normal also.

3. What could and should the company do to see that Amir, Janelle, and the other employees are all treated fairly and responsibly?

The company has a responsibility to be discreet and to maintain confidentiality in handling Janelle's situation, whatever it might be. They will need to make sure that Amir does not try to take on Janelle's problems himself because he is not a trained counselor. Whatever action the Employee Assistance Program (EAP) takes, someone needs to follow up with Janelle, allow time to pass for the problem to resolve, and keep the lines of communication open.

If this is a case of domestic violence, the company needs to be responsible enough to protect the other employees from any potential incidents that might result, i.e., an irate husband coming into the workplace.

■ ADDITIONAL ACTIVITY

Intervention Role-Play

Purpose: To help students understand how managers can deal appropriately and effectively with employees' personal problems that may be affecting the workplace.

The Case: Gwen has been managing eight employees in a small interior design division of a furniture manufacturing company for five years now. She likes the job and feels that all of her employees are talented and skilled, which has contributed to the success of the company.

A couple of months ago, Gwen noticed that one of her employees, Tyler, seemed to be talking on the phone a lot more than usual, making personal calls. His appearance also became unkempt. At first, Gwen dismissed his behavior as a temporary lapse, but when his performance began to decline, and he seemed disinterested in his work, she began to think something was wrong. Then, when Tyler began arguing with other employees over trivial issues, and started coming in late to work, Gwen knew she had to do something. Gwen asked Tyler to meet in her office. "Tyler, you seem disinterested in your work lately, and it used to be all you talked about. Is there something going on in your life?" Embarrassed, Tyler stammered, "Uh, no… I've just had some things to take care of at home. I'll deal with it." A week later, Tyler was still distracted and seemed more depressed than usual.

Knowing that a manager is neither a trained counselor nor a therapist, Gwen is considering what action she is going to take. She might allow more time to pass to see if Tyler's situation improves; or she could approach Tyler again and possibly tell him she is going to call the EAP for their company.

Procedure: Have five or six pairs of students each perform this role-play for the rest of the class. Let these student volunteers have some time to write their scripts and plan their presentations. Usually, it is most effective to give them a few days to get together outside of class. Each couple should prepare both a positive and a negative outcome script. If classroom time allows after the presentations, different partners could be switched between the pairs to create new scenarios with their roles.

After all the role-plays are performed, ask the rest of the class for their input. Ask students which approach seemed to be the most or least successful for this situation. Also, ask which scenario had the potential for the best outcome in most situations. This exercise can produce a great deal of positive and engaged discussion, especially since personal problems affect everyone, and most students have known of someone in a troubling situation, experiencing either family conflict, substance abuse problems, financial difficulties, or mental health conditions. As with many role-play activities, the discussion can be the most productive part of the exercise.

If you have time, you might assign two or more larger groups to work independently, to prepare a series of these presentations rather than just one. In that case, your class can also discuss the differences in these presentations.

Closing Thoughts About Human Relations and Your Future

LECTURE OUTLINE

I. Human Relations and Your Future Success

  A. Your Definition of Success

    1. Many changes will take place ten years from now. Much of what happens to the American business environment by then will involve you.

    2. A newer definition of success includes a sense of self-satisfaction and fulfillment at work, with time and freedom to have family life and leisure time. To attract and keep valuable employees, corporations are beginnig to incorporate **intergenerational care** into their benefits packages.

    3. With the growth of the Internet, working at home is taking on dimensions unheard of ten years ago.

  B. Self-Esteem, Self-Confidence, and Success. Positive self-talk and confident behavior can boost self-confidence, which is basic to any success.

  C. Self-Discipline and Success. **Self-discipline** is the ability to teach or guide yourself to set up and carry out goals and plans.

II. Self-Motivation, Self-Direction, and Success. Self-direction is the ability to set **short-term** and **long-term** goals for yourself.

III. Fear: The Enemy of Success

  A. Common types of fear:

    1. The **impostor phenomenon** is being afraid that you are not smart, hardworking, or talented enough to continue to succeed, and that someone will find you out as an impostor.

    2. **Fear of failure** is a common type of fear, which occurs especially when people are afraid of looking bad to others.

    3. **Fear of success** is also common. People who have a fear of success usually have not had much success in their lives and fear they do not deserve it.

  B. Practicing the opposite of your fears can help eliminate them.

IV. Finding Your Niche

  A. You need to find that place where you survive, thrive, and are most content. To do this, you must understand your own strengths and weaknesses.

  B. You can figure out what your skills are by listing what you are good at and what you enjoy doing.

 19.1 Set Short-Term and Long-Term Goals

  1. Start long-term goals by asking thoughtful questions, such as "What do I want out of life?" or "What do I want my life to have meant after I'm gone?"

  2. From this, form a **life mission statement**. It should answer the large questions you've just asked.

  3. Set short-term goals involving finances, education, and personal achievement.

 19.2 Make an Inventory of Your Skills

  1. Health and physical stamina

  2. Quantitative ability and interest level

  3. People skills

  4. Leadership skills

  5. Mechanical ability

  6. Musical ability

  7. Artistic ability

  8. Creativity and discernment

  9. Self-assurance

  10. Speaking and writing ability

  You most likely have talents in one or more of the areas above. The next step is to apply those skills to a specific goal. **Entrepreneurship**, the risk-taking entrance into your own enterprise, might take you into areas of new, unexplored endeavor.

ANSWERS TO IN-CHAPTER QUESTIONS

PHOTO, page 627: What is your personal definition of success?

Answers will vary according to students' individual goals.

PHOTO, page 630: What are the main characteristics of self-discipline?

Self discipline is made up of many factors, including breaking bad habits, forming new ones, and engaging in positive self-talk to help yourself meet goals.

PHOTO, page 633: Have you found your niche yet?

This depends on the student; students will know that they have found their niche if they are content in what they do, feel they were meant to do it, and find themselves often experiencing "flow" (learned about in Chapter 4).

PHOTO, page 636: In what areas of your life can you use the human relations skills you learned in this course?

Students can use human relations skills in all areas! Human relations skills will stay with students and develop throughout life. The tools learned in this class will always be able to provide help and guidance.

CHAPTER REVIEW, pages 638–640

Review Questions

❶ Why is the work–family issue considered so important today? What are some ways employers are dealing with this issue?

People today are more likely to define individual success by self-satisfaction and self-fulfillment, rather than by the bottom line of wealth and material goods that often defined success in previous decades. Self-satisfaction today includes finding a balance between work and family life or leisure activities.

Employers want to keep good employees, so corporate America is changing to better accommodate employees. Employers also realize that the workforce is becoming increasingly female; since mothers are still most likely to be the primary caretaker of dependent children, businesses must meet the needs of working mothers better. Even fathers are asking for more family-focused benefits, such as paternity leave. Many companies are considering adding a "daddy track" for men (similar to the "mommy track" for women) who want to put their families before career advancement.

Employers today are recognizing that stress and family problems can spill over into work, so they are more often offering solutions to family issues in order to lessen their effects on the workplace. This includes offering cafeteria-style benefits that include day care, often for elderly family members as well as children (known as **intergenerational care**). Employers are also more likely to offer flexible work hours (flextime), a compressed workweek, job-sharing, or telecommuting. Employee Assistance Programs (EAPs) also are likely to include counseling for family-related problems.

❷ What is the difference between short-term goals and long-term goals? What are some short- and long-term goals you have set?

Short-term goals are specific smaller goals for the immediate future, while long-term goals are larger goals that you develop after determining your life plans.

Answers will vary. In general, short-term goals probably include things like finishing a specific course, finishing a term paper, finishing a specific work assignment, or cleaning out the storage room at home. Long-term goals are more likely to include things such as completing a business degree, securing a promotion at work in the next year, saving enough money for a down payment on a house, and so on.

❸ What is meant by the Impostor Phenomenon? What is one way to eliminate fears such as this?

The **impostor phenomenon** happens when capable and successful people feel that they have not accomplished their successes on their own, and feel like impostors who will soon be found out as frauds. This is very common in the workplace and in school, and may have a lot to do with other concepts discussed in this course such as low self-esteem. Women who excel in school or in business often report feeling this way (although men may be experiencing it just as often but are less willing to talk about it).

Fears such as this can be eliminated through:
- positive self-talk, such as "I did design this advertising campaign myself, and it was good!" or "I got an 'A' on the exam, and it was a hard test! I'm a good student!"

- accepting credit for one's own successes: "That wasn't just luck. I really worked hard on that paper and I deserved that 'A'."
- practicing emotions that are opposite to fear, since people cannot feel opposite emotions simultaneously (such as fear and relaxation, or fear and happiness).

In some cases, counseling may be necessary for people who are unable to work effectively or are experiencing uncontrollable anxiety because of the impostor phenomenon.

Critical Thinking Questions

4 **What is included in the idea of self-discipline? What are some examples of everyday behaviors that require self-discipline that you are currently engaging in? Can you succeed without these?**

Self-discipline includes the ability to guide yourself in forming and carrying out goals and plans. It is important in accomplishing short-term goals, long-term goals, and future success, because one cannot reach these without some sort of self-discipline. Individuals must be self-disciplined enough to develop and carry out plans of action.

Answers to students' behaviors that require self-discipline will vary, and may include:
- health-related behaviors, such as staying on a diet, setting up a nutrition plan, getting enough sleep, wearing seatbelts in the car, or quitting smoking or drinking.
- work habits, including getting to work on time, finishing assignments on time, or becoming more organized.
- personal habits, like stopping nailbiting, grooming habits, walking the dog regularly, or completing housework.
- school/study habits, including attending all classes, getting to class on time, taking good notes, rewriting notes, listening to lecture tapes, writing down assignments or due dates, setting up a regular study time and place, studying more effectively, getting a study group together, outlining reading material, or making flash cards of vocabulary terms.

Answers will vary.

5 **What is meant by finding your niche? What is one suggestion to help you in doing this? What are you doing in order to find your niche?**

Finding your niche in employment means finding the job or career where you will be most content and most satisfied.

A suggestion to help students find their niche is to understand themselves and determine what their skills are among the "families" of skills (e.g., data, people, or things). Once they have identified their skills by listing the kinds of things they are good at or enjoy doing, they can figure out what types of jobs are best. An example might be realizing you are good at using objects or things, such as tools or machinery, and you really enjoy the challenge of making machinery work, then training for a career as a computer technician instead of a computer data entry clerk or a computer class instructor.

Answers will vary.

19.1 Reluctant Rosa

1. What was the real source of Rosa's fears?

Rosa's initial fears seem to be centered on fear of the unknown. Her anxiety is also focused on fear of losing her position of power, of losing the comfort of the status quo, and possibly of new technology in general (see question #2, below). For another focus, you could refer students back to the issues of personal and organizational change in Chapter 9.

2. What role did fear play in slowing down Rosa's understanding of the new system? What probably would have happened if she had never overcome these fears?

Fear made Rosa feel inadequate and prevented her from enjoying work. Rosa's fear of failure prevented her from attempting to learn the new technology. If Rosa had not overcome this fear, she probably would have lowered her overall work performance.

3. How could Rosa have prevented this fear, or ended it earlier?

Rosa could have signed up for the training sessions earlier when she was informed about the new installation, before her fear of failure grew.

Case Study

19.2 Tita's Skills

1. What kinds of skills are important in the job that Tita is doing now? Does her current job seem to match her skills? If not, how did she end up choosing this field? What kinds of jobs might she be better at?

Tita's current job requires data skills, specifically manipulating information.

Her current job does not seem to match her skills (i.e., what she is good at and enjoys doing), because the part of her job that she really enjoys is contact with people, such as when she trains new employees.

Tita chose her job because it was in a growing field.

Tita would probably be good at a training and employment relations position. She also might be good at any other job that requires people skills, such as sales or public relations.

2. If you were Tita, what kinds of short-term goals and long-term goals would be reasonable to set? Is there any way that Gloria could help in the goal-setting?

Tita should begin to identify her job skills and preferences. She can set some short-term goals, such as identifying a position she would like to attain and finding out how best to prepare for it, then she can begin to carry out the goals she has set. As a long-term goal, Tita can prepare for her ideal job by taking courses, by seeking an internship or on-the-job training, or by beginning a job search that would land her a new job within a specific time frame. She should identify what she would like to be doing in the next five to ten years, then begin a plan of action to reach those goals.

As Tita's immediate supervisor, Gloria has already noticed that Tita is not satisfied in her position. Gloria could help Tita by giving her responsibilities that more closely match her skills, abilities, and preferences. Gloria could also notify Tita of job openings for which she might be better suited.

3. What kinds of fears is Tita facing? How might she get rid of these fears?

In the short term, she probably fears failing at attempting to get a new position or type of job. She also may have a fear of success. Neither of these, however, is immediately clear from the case, but students could suggest that this is so. Students could also argue that she may be experiencing the impostor phenomenon of not feeling comfortable with being successful and capable in her field. She may fear change and the stress that changing to a new job could bring.

Tita needs to get rid of her fears by crediting herself with her own successes, by evaluating herself and taking stock of her abilities and skills, by positive self-talk, and by practicing opposite emotions when she feels fearful or discouraged. If she feels stressed from the changes of a new job or a job search, she could practice relaxation techniques and general stress-reduction strategies (see Chapter 14). She should also practice the strategies discussed in this chapter for finding her niche.

POWERPOINT® INSTRUCTOR PRESENTATION USER'S GUIDE

CD-ROM POWERPOINT® CONTENTS

File Name	Chapter
HR1.ppt	Chapter 1 Human Relations: A Background
HR2.ppt	Chapter 2 Self-Esteem in Human Relations
HR3.ppt	Chapter 3 Self-Awareness and Self-Disclosure
HR4.ppt	Chapter 4 Attitudes
HR5.ppt	Chapter 5 Personal and Organizational Values
HR6.ppt	Chapter 6 Motivation: Increasing Productivity
HR7.ppt	Chapter 7 Communication and Human Relations
HR8.ppt	Chapter 8 People, Groups, and Their Leaders
HR9.ppt	Chapter 9 Teams in Quality Organizations
HR10.ppt	Chapter 10 Transactions and Relationships
HR11.ppt	Chapter 11 Individual and Organizational Change
HR12.ppt	Chapter 12 Creativity and Human Relations
HR13.ppt	Chapter 13 Conflict Management
HR14.ppt	Chapter 14 Stress and Stress Management
HR15.ppt	Chapter 15 Winning and Keeping Your Customers
HR16.ppt	Chapter 16 Managing Diversity
HR17.ppt	Chapter 17 Business Ethics and Social Responsibility
HR18.ppt	Chapter 18 Maintaining Workplace Health
HR19.ppt	Chapter 19 Closing Thoughts About Human Relations and Your Future

USING POWERPOINT® INSTRUCTOR PRESENTATIONS

INTRODUCTION

The enclosed CD-ROM contains 19 PowerPoint Presentations, one presentation for each chapter of *Human Relations: Strategies for Success,* second edition. Designed to be visually appealing, each presentation includes a chapter outline, important headings and concepts, figures from the text, plus graphic organizers to present content in a different way for students who are visual learners. Also included are key terms with pop-up definitions, as well as Strategies for Success and Chapter Review questions.

USING PRESENTATIONS IN THE CLASSROOM

Many teachers have not yet used PowerPoint Presentations in the classroom. The following suggestions may help you if this is your first time using them:

- PowerPoint Presentations are intended to supplement your presentation of the material in the textbook. They are not a substitute for the text or for your stand-up classroom teaching.
- If your school has a wireless mouse for your computer (or another means of advancing slides in PowerPoint Presentations), you can move around the classroom as you teach. This will allow you to focus on an individual student's work and deal with problems before a student falls too far behind.
- Even if your class does not have a wireless mouse, you will only need to return to your computer to advance the presentation one slide at a time with one keystroke. You will not be tied to the computer as you go through a procedure in front of the class.
- Using PowerPoint Presentations, you will never lose track of transparencies in front of the class and spend valuable time getting them back in order.

Ultimately, these PowerPoint Instructor Presentations can make your job easier, accelerate learning, and allow for more individualized teaching.

RUNNING POWERPOINT® INSTRUCTOR PRESENTATIONS

SETTING UP YOUR EQUIPMENT

Before you begin using PowerPoint Instructor Presentations, check your equipment connections. To use PowerPoint Instructor Presentations, you will need a computer (see System Requirements) and a projector or large screen monitor capable of displaying high-color images.

LOADING THE PRESENTATIONS

The PowerPoint Instructor Presentations files have not been compressed; therefore, they can be run directly from the CD-ROM. In most cases, the PowerPoint Instructor Presentations will run faster if loaded on your hard drive. If you load the presentations on your hard drive, you may wish to organize them in a separate folder.

RUNNING A PRESENTATION WITH POWERPOINT

The best way to run a PowerPoint Instructor Presentation is with PowerPoint software. The following instructions assume that PowerPoint is located on your hard disk, and that the extension ".ppt" is recognized by your computer as a PowerPoint Presentation.

1. In the Explorer, open the folder containing the PowerPoint Presentations.
2. Double-click the PowerPoint Presentation you wish to view.
3. Run the presentation as a slide show. You could either click the *Slide Show* button or choose the *Slide Show* from the *View* menu.
4. The following table lists the ways to move to the Next and Previous slides, using the keyboard.

Running a Presentation	
NEXT SLIDE	**PREVIOUS SLIDE**
→ right arrow button	← left arrow button
↓ down arrow button	↑ up arrow button
N button	P button
ENTER button	BACKSPACE button
SPACE bar	
Click left mouse	

RUNNING A PRESENTATION WITH POWERPOINT VIEWER

If you do not have PowerPoint 97, you can go to Microsoft's home page (www.microsoft.com) to download a free PowerPoint viewer. Once this viewer has been installed, follow these directions:

1. Make sure your monitor is set to high-color mode. If your screen is not set properly, right click on the *Desktop*, choose *Properties*, and change the monitor settings.
2. Click the Start menu button and choose the *Programs* option.
3. Select *Microsoft PowerPoint Viewer* to start the Viewer program.
4. Click the *Look in:* pop-up menu and select your CD-ROM drive.
5. Choose the PowerPoint Presentation you wish to view.
6. When you start a presentation you will see an opening slide. Click the *Forward* button to proceed to the next slide.
7. From the *Contents* (or Main menu) slide you can access almost all of the PowerPoint Presentations resources. While viewing a presentation, click the navigation button to view the slide. Click the *Help* button for step-by-step instructions.
8. To end the presentation, click the *Exit* button or press the *Esc* (escape) key.

CUSTOMIZING A PRESENTATION

The PowerPoint Instructor Presentations were created using Microsoft PowerPoint 97 (Windows). Although you do not need PowerPoint to view the slides, you can customize any of the presentations if you have PowerPoint 97 (or a later version). Follow the steps provided in the *Help* system.

TROUBLESHOOTING TIPS

If you experience problems using PowerPoint Presentations, refer to the troubleshooting tips in the *Help* system. A comprehensive list of potential problems is provided along with suggested solutions. To access this information, start a presentation and click on the *Help* button. Select *Microsoft PowerPoint Help* and type in your question.

SYSTEM REQUIREMENTS

Verify that your computer meets the hardware and software requirements listed below:

Hardware:
- IBM PC or 100% compatible computer
- 386 or higher microprocessor
- 4× CD-ROM
- 8 MB of hard disk for "Typical" installation; "Custom" or "Complete" installation can require up to 35 MB
- VGA or higher-resolution video monitor (SVGA 256-color recommended) Mouse
- Printer (optional, but recommended)

Software:
- PowerPoint 7 for Windows 95, PowerPoint 97 or higher, or PowerPoint Viewer
- Windows 95 or later

EXAMVIEW PRO® TESTBANK GENERATOR USER'S GUIDE

TO THE TEACHER

The Examview Pro 3.5 Testbank Generator for Glencoe's *Human Relations: Strategies for Success*, second edition, allows you to generate readymade and customized objective tests using multiple choice, true or false, and essay questions. Grouped by cognitive type within each chapter, the questions cover all 19 chapters and 4 units in the *Human Relations: Strategies for Success*, second edition, text.

LEARNING OBJECTIVES

Learning objectives are suggested outcomes of what your students may be capable of achieving during or after your teaching. The objectives for each chapter (the same ones found in the Student Edition) are listed in this manual.

COMPONENTS

Components of the ExamView Pro 3.5 Testbank Generator for *Human Relations: Strategies for Success*, second edition, include:

- ExamView Pro 3.5 Testbank Generator *User's Guide* (Windows/Macintosh)
- ExamView Pro 3.5 Testbank Generator CD-ROM Software (Windows/Macintosh)

The following User's Guide contains instructions for the setup and use of the testbank generator. Be sure to use the correct guide for your system (Windows or Macintosh). The CD-ROM Software contains the testbank generator program that lets you retrieve the questions you want and print tests. It also lets you edit and add questions as needed.

SITE LICENSE

Your adoption of Glencoe's second edition of *Human Relations: Strategies for Success* entitles you to site-license duplication rights for all components of the ExamView Pro 3.5 Testbank Generator with the restriction that all copies must be used within the adopting schools. This license shall run for the life of the adoption of the accompanying text.

USING THE TESTBANK

Before you begin, follow the directions in the *User's Guide* to make backup copies of the software. Then, set up your computer and printer and configure the software, following the instructions. The **User's Guide** contains all the instructions on how to use the software. Refer to this manual as needed to preview and select questions for your tests.

SOFTWARE SUPPORT HOTLINE

Should you encounter any difficulty when setting up or running the programs, contact the Software Support Center at Glencoe Publishing between 8:30 A.M. and 6:00 P.M. Eastern Time. The toll-free number is **1-800-437-3715**. Customers with specific questions can contact us via the Internet at the following E-mail address: **epgtech@mcgraw-hill.com**.

LEARNING OBJECTIVES TESTED

Chapter 1

1. Define human relations.
2. Know the importance of human relations to success in business.
3. Learn a short history of the study of human relations.
4. Know the challenges of human relations in today's workplace.
5. Know which traits are most helpful to effective human relations.

Chapter 2

1. Understand the importance of self-esteem.
2. Understand the relationship between self-esteem and work performance.
3. Distinguish different types of self-esteem.
4. Explain the origin of you self-esteem.
5. Identify the different areas of the self-concept.
6. Build up your own self-esteem, and identify low self-esteem in others.
7. Combat low self-esteem.

Chapter 3

1. Understand self-disclosure and its relationship to personal relationships and the workplace.
2. Use the Johari Window as a tool for self-understanding.
3. Avoid the pitfalls that prevent self-disclosure.
4. Avoid overdisclosure.
5. Understand the five major levels of communication.
6. Overcome the fear of self-disclosure.

Chapter 4

1. Understand what makes up attitudes, and how people get attitudes.
2. Examine what goes into making a positive, or healthy, attitude.
3. See the connection between positive attitudes and self-esteem.
4. Find activities that provide optimal experiences.
5. Appreciate the link between positive attitudes and job satisfaction.
6. Understand the importance of positive attitudes to the rest of your life.

Chapter 5

1. Learn where personal and organizational values originate.
2. Understand why values are important both individually and organizationally.
3. Identify your personal values and those in your organization.
4. Test your personal values to see if they are really your own.
5. Identify values systems and grow from that knowledge.
6. Learn to understand and apply the value of integrity.
7. Learn to understand values in a global context.

Chapter 6

1. Understand how most people are motivated.
2. Recognize the importance of organizational climate and morale.
3. See the difference between extrinsic and intrinsic motivators.
4. Use praise to improve motivation.
5. See how needs drive motivation.
6. Understand the relationship between self-esteem and motivation.

Chapter 7

1. Understand the crucial role of communication at work.
2. Appreciate the value of listening skills as human relations tools.
3. Examine the role of nonverbal communication.
4. Understand the dynamics of formal and informal channels of communication.
5. Appreciate the importance of intercultural communication in today's business world.

Chapter 8

1. Understand the operation of group dynamics within organizations.
2. Recognize and avoid the many pitfalls of group dynamics.
3. Understand leadership and leadership styles.
4. Understand leadership power and how to strengthen your power.

Chapter 9

1. Understand the history, foundations, and major points of Total Quality Management (TQM)
2. Know why TQM has been influential in the U.S. and Japan.
3. Put team-building steps into place.
4. Distinguish between the models of decision making in teams.
5. Make teamwork successful.
6. Improve the organizational climate of the workplace.
7. Distinguish between different types of corporate culture.
8. See the value in the "new" corporate culture, and its link to self-esteem.

Chapter 10

1. Understand the basic principles and practices of transactional analysis, including ego states, transactions, scripts, games, and life positions.
2. Learn how to make emotional decisions more rationally.
3. Encourage complementary transactions to take place more often.
4. Identify and put an end to games in the workplace.

Chapter 11

1. Recognize the stages of change in the process of suffering and repair.
2. Manage effective changes in an organization.
3. Use change models to aid the change process in organizations.
4. Identify and overcome the enemies of change in the workplace.
5. Understand the function of organizational development in the formal change process.

Chapter 12

1. Know what is meant by creativity.
2. Compare how creativity is different from intelligence.
3. Learn how creativity can be increased.
4. Explain why creativity is important in the workplace.
5. Understand the link between creativity and self-esteem.

Chapter 13

1. Identify major types and sources of conflict.
2. Use the collaborative method of conflict management.
3. Discover how to negotiate a win–win solution to conflicts.
4. Understand and use the Thomas–Kilman Conflict Model.
5. Deal effectively with personality types that create destructive conflict.

Chapter 14

1. Recognize the sources of stress in your life.
2. Discover how stress affects your physical and mental health.
3. Reduce and manage stress.
4. Take care of yourself for life.
5. Understand why stress is a problem in the workplace.
6. See the link between stress and self-esteem.

Chapter 15

1. Learn how good customer relations leads to success.
2. Develop the skill of encouraging customers to complain.
3. Understand the relationship between self-esteem and customer relations.
4. Learn how to tell customers bad news without losing their business.
5. Develop skills that help you relate to difficult customers.
6. Understand why your customers should not make your decisions.

Chapter 16

1. Know what is meant by diversity in the workplace.
2. Identify the possible sources or causes of prejudice and discrimination.
3. Recognize targets of prejudice or discrimination.
4. Recognize and prevent sexual harassment in the workplace.
5. Work with diverse groups of people and reduce conflict.

Chapter 17

1. Know whether a business practice is ethical or unethical.
2. Recognize five principles on which ethical codes are founded.
3. Explain how ethics can be affected by one's workgroup.
4. Recognize different cultural practices in foreign countries.
5. Understand how social responsibility relates to ethics at work.
6. Know how to deal with unethical conduct in business.

Chapter 18

1. See how the effects of substance abuse and other behaviors detract from workplace health.
2. Recognize behaviors that reduce workplace health.
3. Know what employers/employees can do to help substance abuse, personal or financial situations, and medical conditions.

Chapter 19

1. Explore the concept of success and the attainment of goals.
2. Consider the importance of self-esteem and self-discipline in the attainment of goals.
3. Examine the problem of fear and how it can hamper your success.
4. Find your "niche" in connection with human relations.

SECTION 1 — INTRODUCTION

This user's guide accompanies a test generator program called *ExamView*® *Pro 3.5*–an application that enables you to quickly create printed tests, Internet tests, and computer (LAN-based) tests. You can enter your own questions and customize the appearance of the tests you create. The *ExamView Pro* test generator program offers many unique features. Using the QuickTest wizard, for example, you are guided step-by-step through the process of building a test. Numerous options are included that allow you to customize the content and appearance of the tests you create.

As you work with the *ExamView* test generator, you may use the following features:

- **an interview mode or "wizard" to guide you through the steps to create a test in less than five minutes**
- **five methods to select test questions**
    - random selection
    - from a list
    - while viewing questions
    - by criteria (difficulty code, objective, topic, etc.–if available)
    - all questions
- **the capability to edit questions or to add an unlimited number of questions**
- **online (*Internet-based*) testing**
    - create a test that students can take on the Internet using a browser
    - receive instant feedback via email
    - create online study guides with student feedback for incorrect responses
    - include any of the twelve (12) question types
- **Internet test-hosting ***
    - instantly publish a test to the *ExamView* Web site
    - manage tests online
    - allow students to access tests from one convenient location
    - receive detailed reports
    - download results to your gradebook or spreadsheet
- **online (*LAN-based*) testing**
    - allow anyone or selected students to take a test on your local area network
    - schedule tests
    - create online study guides with student feedback for incorrect responses
    - incorporate multimedia links (movies and audio)
    - export student results to a gradebook or spreadsheet
- **a sophisticated word processor**
    - streamlined question entry with spell checker
    - tabs, fonts, symbols, foreign characters, and text styles
    - tables with borders and shading
    - full-featured equation editor
    - pictures or other graphics within a question, answer, or narrative
- **numerous test layout and printing options**
    - scramble the choices in multiple choice questions
    - print multiple versions of the same test with corresponding answer keys
    - print an answer key strip for easier test grading
- **link groups of questions to common narratives**

* The Internet test-hosting service must be purchased separately. Visit www.examview.com to learn more.

SECTION 2 — INSTALLATION AND STARTUP INSTRUCTIONS

The *ExamView Pro 3.5* test generator software is provided on a CD-ROM or floppy disks. The disc includes the program and all of the questions for the corresponding textbook. The *ExamView Player,* which can be used by your students to take online (computerized or LAN-based) tests, is also included.

Before you can use the test generator, you must install it on your hard drive. The system requirements, installation instructions, and startup procedures are provided below.

SYSTEM REQUIREMENTS

To use the *ExamView Pro 3.5* test generator or the online test player, your computer must meet or exceed the following minimum hardware requirements:

Windows

- Pentium computer
- Windows 95, Windows 98, Windows 2000 (or a more recent version)
- color monitor (VGA-compatible)
- CD-ROM and/or high-density floppy disk drive
- hard drive with at least 7 MB space available
- 8 MB available memory *(16 MB memory recommended)*
- an Internet connection to access the Internet test-hosting features

Macintosh

- PowerPC processor, 100 MHz computer
- System 7.5 (or a more recent version)
- color monitor (VGA-compatible)
- CD-ROM and/or high-density floppy disk drive
- hard drive with at least 7 MB space available
- 8 MB available memory *(16 MB memory recommended)*
- an Internet connection with System 8.6 (or more recent version) to access the Internet test-hosting features

INSTALLATION INSTRUCTIONS

Follow these steps to install the *ExamView* test generator software. The setup program will automatically install everything you need to use *ExamView.* **Note:** A separate test player setup program is also included for your convenience. [See *Online (LAN-based) Testing* on page 149 for more information.]

Windows

Step 1
Turn on your computer.

Step 2
Insert the *ExamView* disc into the CD-ROM drive. If the program is provided on floppy disks, insert Disk 1 into Drive A.

Step 3
Click the **Start** button on the *Taskbar* and choose the *Run* option.

Step 4

If the *ExamView* software is provided on a CD-ROM, use the drive letter that corresponds to the CD-ROM drive on your computer (e.g., **d:\setup.exe**). The setup program, however, may be located in a subfolder on the CD-ROM if the *ExamView* software is included on the disc with other resources. In which case, click the **Browse** button in the Run dialog box to locate the setup program (e.g., **d:\evpro\setup.exe**).

If you are installing the software from floppy disks, type **a:\setup** and press **Enter** to run the installation program.

Step 5

Follow the prompts on the screen to complete the installation process.

If the software and question banks are provided on more than one floppy disk, you will be prompted to insert the appropriate disk when it is needed.

Step 6

Remove the installation disc when you finish.

Macintosh

Step 1

Turn on your computer.

Step 2

Insert the *ExamView* installation disc into your CD-ROM drive. If the program is provided on floppy disks, insert Disk 1 into a disk drive.

Step 3

Open the installer window, if necessary.

Step 4

Double-click the installation icon to start the program.

Step 5

Follow the prompts on the screen to complete the installation process.

If the software and question banks are provided on more than one floppy disk, you will be prompted to insert the appropriate disk when it is needed.

Step 6

Remove the installation disc when you finish.

GETTING STARTED

After you complete the installation process, follow these instructions to start the *ExamView* test generator software. This section also explains the options used to create a test and edit a question bank.

Startup Instructions

Step 1

Turn on the computer.

Step 2

Windows: Click the **Start** button on the *Taskbar.* Highlight the **Programs** menu and locate the *ExamView Test Generator* folder. Select the *ExamView Pro* option to start the software.

Macintosh: Locate and open the *ExamView* folder. Double-click the *ExamView Pro* program icon.

Step 3

The first time you run the software you will be prompted to enter your name, school/institution name, and city/state. You are now ready to begin using the *ExamView* software.

Step 4

Each time you start *ExamView,* the **Startup** menu appears. Choose one of the options shown in Figure 1. **Note:** All of the figures shown in this user's guide are taken from the Windows software. Except for a few minor differences, the Macintosh screens are identical.

Step 5

Use *ExamView* to create a test or edit questions in a question bank.

ExamView includes three components: Test Builder, Question Bank Editor, and Test Player. The **Test Builder** includes options to create, edit, print, and save tests. The **Question Bank Editor** lets you create or edit question banks. The **Test Player** is a separate program that your students can use to take online (LAN-based) tests/study guides.

Figure 1 – ExamView Startup Menu

Using The Help System

Whenever you need assistance using *ExamView,* access the extensive help system. Click the **Help** button or choose the **Help Topics** option from the *Help* menu to access step-by-step instructions from more than 150 help topics. If you experience any difficulties while you are working with the software, you may want to review the troubleshooting tips in the user-friendly help system.

Test Builder

The Test Builder allows you to create tests using the QuickTest Wizard or you can create a new test on your own. (See the sample test in Figure 2.) Use the Test Builder to prepare both printed and online tests/study guides.

- *If you want ExamView to select questions randomly from one or more question banks,* choose the *QuickTest Wizard* option to create a new test. (Refer to Figure 1 on page 4.) Then, follow the step-by-step instructions to (1) enter a test title, (2) choose one or more question banks from which to select questions, and (3) identify how many questions you want on the test. The QuickTest Wizard will automatically create a new test and use the Test Builder to display the test on screen. You can print the test as is, remove questions, add new questions, or edit any question.
- *If you want to create a new test on your own,* choose the option to create a new test. (Refer to Figure 1 on page 144.) Then identify a question bank from which to choose questions by using the *Question Bank* option in the **Select** menu. You may then add questions to the test by using one or more of the following selection options: *Randomly, From a List, While Viewing, By Criteria,* or *All Questions.*

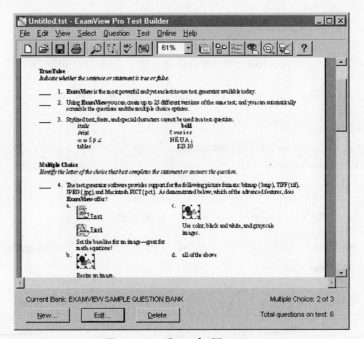

Figure 2 – Sample Test

IMPORTANT: The Test Builder and the Question Bank Editor systems are integrated in one program. As you work with *ExamView*, you can easily switch between the Test Builder and Question Bank Editor components using the *Switch to...* option in the **File** menu.

To create a new test:

Step 1

Start the *ExamView* software.

Step 2

At the Startup window, choose the *Create a new test* option.

Step 3

Enter a title for the new test.

After you enter the title, the program will automatically display the option for you to select a question bank.

Step 4

Choose a question bank.

Step 5

Select the questions you want to include on the test.

Use the question selection options that appear in the **Select** menu. Or, click the corresponding buttons on the toolbar. A description for each of the question selection toolbar buttons appears below.

 Click the **Question Bank** toolbar button to select a question bank.

You can create a test using questions from one question bank or from multiple banks. Choose a bank, select the questions you want, and then choose another bank to select more questions.

 Click the **Select Randomly** toolbar button when you want the program to randomly select questions for you.

 Use the **Select from a List** command to choose questions if you know which ones you want to select. Identify the questions you want by reviewing a question bank printout.

 Click the **Select while Viewing** button to display a window that shows all of the questions in the current question bank. Click the check boxes to select the questions you want.

 You can use the **Select by Criteria** option to choose questions based on question type, difficulty, and objective (if available).

 Click the **Select All** button to choose all of the questions in the current question bank.

Step 6

Save the test.

Step 7

Print the test.

You can use the options in the **Test** menu to customize the appearance of a test, edit test instructions, and choose to leave space for students to write their answers. When you print a test, you may choose how many variations of the test you want, whether you want all the versions to be the same, and whether you want to scramble the questions and the multiple choice options. If you choose to scramble the questions, *ExamView* will print a custom answer sheet for each variation of the test.

If you want your students to take a test online, first create the test. Then, publish the test as an Internet test/study guide (page 155) or use the Online Test Wizard (page 150) to create a test for delivery over a LAN (local area network). The software will walk you through the steps to turn any test into an online (Internet or LAN-based) test.

IMPORTANT: You may edit questions or create new questions as you build your test. However, those questions can be used only as part of the current test. If you plan to create several new questions that you would like to use on other tests, switch to the Question Bank Editor to add the new questions.

Question Bank Editor

The Question Bank Editor allows you to edit questions in an existing publisher-supplied question bank or to create your own new question banks. Always use the Question Bank Editor if you want to change a question permanently in an existing question bank. If you want to make a change that applies only to a particular test, create a new question or edit that question in the Test Builder.

A question bank may include up to 250 questions in a variety of formats including multiple choice, true/false, modified true/false, completion, yes/no, matching, problem, essay, short answer, case, and numeric response. You can include the following information for each question: difficulty code, reference, text objective, state objectives, topic, and notes.

Step 1
Start the *ExamView* software.

Step 2
At the Startup window as illustrated in Figure 1 on page 144, choose to *Create a new question bank* or *Open an existing question bank*.

If you are working in the Test Builder, click the **File** menu and choose *Switch to Question Bank Editor* to edit or create a new question bank.

Step 3
Click the **New** button to create a new question or click the **Edit** button to modify an existing question. Both of these buttons appear at the bottom of the Question Bank Editor window. (See Figure 3.)

You may add new questions or edit questions in a question bank by using the built-in word processor. The word processor includes many features commonly found in commercially available word processing applications. These features include the following: fonts, styles, tables, paragraph formatting, ruler controls, tabs, indents, and justification.

Step 4
Save your work. Then, exit the program or switch back to the Test Builder.

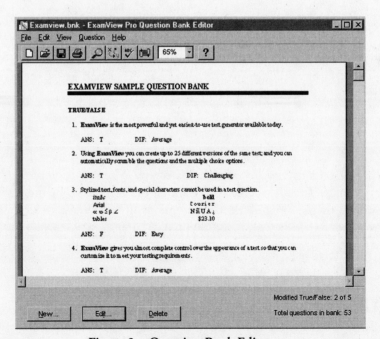

Figure 3 – Question Bank Editor

Online Testing (LAN-based vs. Internet)

The *ExamView* software allows you to create paper tests and online tests. The program provides two distinct online testing options: **LAN-based** testing and **Internet** testing. The option you choose depends on your particular testing needs. You can choose either option to administer online tests and study guides.

The **LAN-based** testing option is designed to work on a local area network server. That is, you can copy the test/study guide along with the Test Player software onto your local area network. Then students can take the test at computers connected to your server.

To take a LAN-based test you must provide access for your students to the Test Player program included with the *ExamView* software. The Test Player is a separate program that lets your students take a test/study guide at a computer. You can store the Test Player program and the test on a local area network for easy access by your students.

The **Internet** testing option provides a computerized testing solution for delivering tests via the Internet or an Intranet. This option is great for distance learning environments or simply to make a sample test/study guide available to students at home. Students do not need any other program (unlike the LAN-based option). When your students take a test, the results are automatically sent to you via email.

You can publish an Internet test to your own Web site, or you can use the *ExamView* Internet test-hosting service. If you subscribe to the *ExamView* test-hosting service, you can publish a test directly to the Internet with just a few simple steps. Students will have immediate access to the tests that you publish and you can get detailed reports. For more information on the Internet test-hosting service, visit our Web site at www.examview.com.

SECTION 3 — ONLINE (LAN-BASED) TESTING

Online testing features are seamlessly integrated into the *ExamView* software. If you want to take advantage of these capabilities, simply create a test and then use the Online Test Wizard to setup the testing parameters. Students can then take the test at the computer using the Test Player program.

IMPORTANT: If you want to prepare a test/study guide for delivery via the Internet, use the *Publish Internet Test* option as described on page 156.

ExamView includes many features that let you customize an online (LAN-based) test. You can create a test for a specific class, or you can prepare a study guide for anyone to take. Using the Online Test Wizard, you can schedule a test or allow it to be taken anytime. As your students work on a test, *ExamView* will scramble the question order, provide feedback for incorrect responses, and display a timer if you selected any of these options.

ONLINE (LAN-BASED) TESTING OVERVIEW

Refer to the steps below for an overview of the online (LAN-based) testing process. Specific instructions for creating a test, taking a test, and viewing results are provided on the following pages.

Step 1

Talk with your network administrator to help you setup a location (folder) on your local area network where you can install the Test Player software and copy your tests/study guides.

Make sure that the administrator gives you and your students full access to the designated folders on the server. You may also want your network administrator to install the Test Player software.

Step 2

Create a test/study guide, and then use the Online Test Wizard to setup the online (LAN-based) test. Save your work and exit the *ExamView* software.

Step 3

Transfer the test/study guide file [e.g., chapter1.tst (Windows) or Chapter 1 (Macintosh)] and any accompanying multimedia files from your computer to the local area network server.

Copy the files from your hard drive to the folder setup by your network administrator. You need only copy the test file unless you linked an audio or video segment to one or more questions.

Step 4

Instruct your students to complete the test/study guide.

Students must have access to a computer connected to the local area network on which the Test Player and test/study guide are stored.

Step 5

After all students finish taking the test, copy the test/study guide file back to your hard drive. It is recommended that you copy the test to a different location from the original test file. The test file, itself, contains all of the students' results.

Note: If you set up a class roster, the test file will contain item analysis information and the results for each student. If you did not setup a roster, no results are recorded so you do not have to complete this step or the next.

Step 6

Start the *ExamView* software and open the test file to view your students' results.

CREATING AN ONLINE (LAN-BASED) TEST

Follow the steps shown below to create an online (LAN-based) test or study guide. Depending on the options you set, you can create a test or study guide. Before you begin, make sure that you installed the *ExamView* test generator and test player software. **Note:** See the next section (page 152) for instructions to setup the test player. (See page 155 for Internet testing features.)

Step 1

Start the *ExamView* software.

Step 2

Create or open a test/study guide.

Select the questions you want to include on the test. You can include any of the following types: True/False, Multiple Choice, Yes/No, Numeric Response, Completion, and Matching.

Step 3

Select the *Online Test Wizard* option from the **Online** menu.

ExamView presents step-by-step instructions to help you prepare the online test/study guide. (See Figure 4.) Read the instructions provided and complete each step. **Note:** Click the **Help** button if you need more assistance.

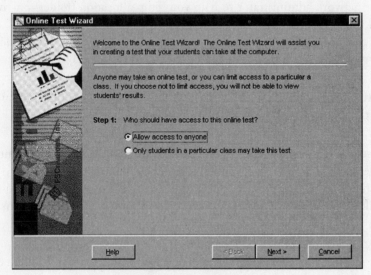

Figure 4 – Online Test Wizard (Step 1)

Step 4

Click the **Finish** button after you complete the last step using the Online Test Wizard. As you can see in Figure 5 on page 151, *ExamView* shows a summary that describes the settings for the online test.

Step 5

Save the test/study guide to a location where your students can easily access it. For example, save it in the same location where you installed the Test Player program.

It is recommended that you save the test/study guide to a location on a network server where students have read/write access. The Test Player will store all of your students' results (if you entered a class roster) in the test file itself. You can copy the test to individual computers, but this configuration takes more time to gather the results.

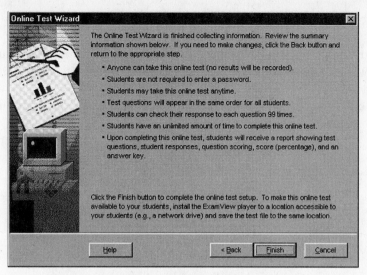

Figure 5 – Online Test Wizard (Summary)

Step 6

If you included multimedia links in any of the questions, copy those files to the same location where you saved the test/study guide.

If the multimedia files are on a CD-ROM or DVD disc, you may leave them on the disc, but provide this information to your students. To play one of these links, they will have to specify the location of the multimedia file.

NOTES:

- Use the *Test Preferences* and *Class Roster* options in the **Online** menu if you want to make any changes to the test parameters. These two options let you change any of the settings you selected using the Online Test Wizard.
- You must close the test before your students can access it with the Test Player.
- If you setup a class roster for a test/study guide, you cannot modify the test (e.g., edit a question, change the order, etc.) once any student has taken it unless you clear the results first.
- Provide your students with the Test Player setup program and a copy of the test/study guide if you want them to take it at home.

INSTALLING THE TEST PLAYER

Follow the instructions provided here to install the Test Player program for your students. You may copy the Test Player to a network (recommended), install it on individual computers, or provide it on floppy disk for your students to take home.

Even if you have a network, you can install the Test Player on individual computers. Students will still be able to access tests/study guides you store on a local area network.

ExamView Player Installation

Windows

Step 1
Turn on your computer.

Step 2
Insert the *ExamView* disc into your CD-ROM drive. If the software was provided on floppy disks, insert the *ExamView–Test Player* installation disk into Drive A.

Step 3
Click the **Start** button on the *Taskbar* and choose the *Run* option.

Step 4
If the *ExamView* software is provided on a CD-ROM, use the drive letter that corresponds to the CD-ROM drive on your computer (e.g., **d:\evplayer\setup** or **d:\evpro\evplayer\setup**).

If you are installing the software from a floppy disk, type **a:\setup** and press **Enter** to run the installation program.

Step 5
When prompted for a location to install the program, select a folder (e.g., x:\programs\evplayer **for network installations or c:\evplayer** on your local hard drive).

Step 6
For local area network (**LAN**) installations, complete the following steps at each workstation:
Click the **Start** button and choose **Taskbar** from the *Settings* menu.
Click the **Start Menu Programs** tab and click **Add**.
Type the location and program name for the Test Player software, or use the **Browse** button to enter this information (e.g., x:\programs\evplayer\evplayer.exe).
Proceed to the next screen and add a new folder (e.g., ExamView Test Player).
Enter ExamView Test Player **as the shortcut name and then click the** Finish **button.**

Repeat Steps 1–5 if you plan to install the software at each computer instead of installing the program once on your network.

Macintosh

Step 1
Turn on your computer.

Step 2
Insert the *ExamView* installation disc into your CD-ROM drive. If the program is provided on floppy disks, insert the *ExamView–Test Player* installation disk into a disk drive.

Step 3
Open the installer window, if necessary.

Step 4
Double-click the installation icon to start the program.

Note: The installation program is configured to copy the test player to a new folder on your hard drive. You can, however, change this location. For example, you can select a location on your network server.

Step 5
When prompted for a location to install the program, select a folder on your local area network that is accessible to all students. If you are installing the software on a stand-alone computer, choose a location on the hard drive.

Step 6
At each workstation, enable file sharing and program linking if you installed the application on your network server.

For stand-alone computers, repeats Steps 1–5.

Installing the Test Player at Home

You can give your students the Test Player software to take home. If the *ExamView* software was sent to you on floppy disks, give your students the separate Test Player setup disk. If you received the software on CD-ROM, copy all of the setup files in the **evplayer** folder onto a floppy disk. Students should follow Steps 1–5 to install the software on their computer. When students take a test home, he/she should copy it into the same folder as the Test Player program.

TAKING AN ONLINE (LAN-BASED) TEST

Make sure that you have properly installed the *ExamView* Test Player software and copied the test/study guide to a location easily accessible to your students. If you linked multimedia files to any of the questions, it is recommended that you copy those files to the same folder as the test/study guide.

If you created a test with a class roster, students must correctly enter their ID's to be able to take the test/study guide. Provide this information to your students, if necessary. **Note:** If you do not want to track student scores, you should set up a test to allow anyone to take it.

Step 1
Start the *ExamView* Test Player software.

Step 2
Enter your name and ID. (See Figure 6.)

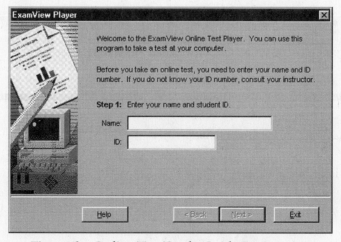

Figure 6 – Online Test/Study Guide Registration

Step 3

Select a test/study guide. (See Figure 7.)

If no tests (or study guides) appear in the list, click the **Folder** button to identify where the tests are located.

Step 4

(Optional) Enter a password, if prompted.

Step 5

Review the summary information and click **Start** when you are ready to begin.

Step 6

Answer all of the questions and click the **End** button when you finish.

Verify that you want to end the test. If you do not answer all of the questions in one session, you will not be able to resume the test at a later time.

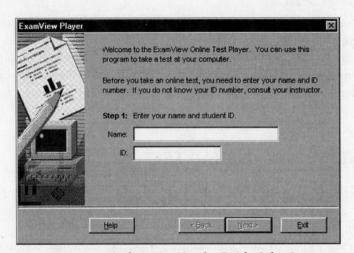

Figure 7 – Online Test/Study Guide Selection

Step 7

Review the test report.

Step 8

Click **New Test** to take another test or click **Exit** to quit the program.

VIEWING ONLINE (LAN-BASED) RESULTS

If you set up a test with a class roster (instead of allowing anyone to access a test/study guide), the *ExamView* Test Player will automatically collect the results for each student. The program saves this information in the test/study guide file itself.

Step 1

Start the *ExamView* software and open the online test/study guide that your students have already taken.

Step 2

Choose *View Test Results* from the Online menu.

Step 3

Review the results, item-by-item analysis, and statistics reports.

Step 4

Choose *Export Test Results* if you want to export the scores to your favorite gradebook program or spreadsheet application.

SECTION 4 — INTERNET TESTING

ExamView lets you easily create Internet tests and study guides. Build a test and then simply choose the *Publish Internet Test* option. You can choose to post tests to your own Web site, or publish tests directly to the ExamView Web site. (Visit us at www.examview.com to learn more about subscribing to the Internet test-hosting service.)

With the Internet test-hosting feature, you can publish a test or study guide directly to the ExamView website. Simply create a test and then follow the easy step-by-step instructions to publish it to the Internet. It's that simple! You can manage tests online, view reports, and download results. Students access your tests from one convenient location.

If you do not use the ExamView test-hosting service, you can manually post tests/study guides to your own Web site. If you create a test, your students' results are sent to you via email automatically. Or, you can create a study guide that your students can use to review various topics at their own pace.

INTERNET TESTING FAQs

Review the FAQs (frequently asked questions) below for more information on the Internet testing hosting features available to *ExamView Pro 3.5* users.

What are the advantages to using the Internet test-hosting feature? (1) Publishing an Internet test to your own Web site and setting up links can be quite challenging. With the Internet test-hosting feature, the process is completely automated. In minutes, you can post a test to the Internet. (2) When you post tests/study guides to your own Web site, only a few options are available. Using the *ExamView* test-hosting service, you have many more options available such as setting up a class roster and viewing detailed item analysis reports.

How do you register for the test-hosting service? Visit our Web site at www.examview.com to learn how to register. Before you can post tests/study guides, you must sign up to obtain a valid instructor ID and a password.

Is there an additional charge for the Internet test-hosting service? Yes, there is an additional yearly subscription charge to use this service. If you received the *ExamView* software from a publisher, you may be eligible for a discount or a free trial membership. (See our Web site for current prices and special promotions.)

Do you have to use the Internet test-hosting service? No, using the test-hosting service is not required. *The Publish Internet Test* feature includes an option to save an Internet test/study guide to a local hard drive. Then, you can manually post it to your own Web site.

Why aren't the same features available for tests posted to my own Web site? To offer the numerous Internet test-hosting features, we have developed many programs and databases that are stored on our servers. If you post to your own server or Web site, these programs are not available.

IMPORTANT: Your students must use a browser such as Netscape 4.0/Internet Explorer 4.0 (or a more recent version) that supports cascading style sheets (CSS1) and JavaScript. To post tests or study guides for delivery via the Internet, you must have your own access to an Internet server.

USING THE INTERNET TEST-HOSTING SERVICE

Using the *ExamView* test generator software you can publish tests directly to the ExamView Web site if you have signed up for the test-hosting service. With a few simple steps, you can publish tests and study guides directly to the Internet. Refer to the following instructions to: register for the Internet test-hosting service, create a test, publish a test to the Internet, take tests online, manage tests, and view student results.

Register for the Internet Test-Hosting Service

Step 1
Launch your Web browser and go to www.examview.com.

Step 2
Go to the **Instructor Center** to register for the test-hosting service. Follow the instructions provided at the Web site to sign up.

Record the instructor ID and password assigned to you. You will need this information to publish a test or study guide to the *ExamView* Web site. When you choose to publish a test, you will be prompted to enter this information.

Step 3
Quit the browser.

Publish a Test/Study Guide to the ExamView Web Site

Step 1
Start the *ExamView* software.

Step 2
Create a new test or open an existing test.

Select the questions you want to include on the test. You can include any of the twelve (12) question types on a test, but only the objective questions are scored.

Step 3
Select the *Publish Internet Test* option from the **File** menu.

ExamView presents a window with various Internet testing options to help you prepare the online test. (See Figure 8.) **Note:** Click the **Help** button if you need more assistance.

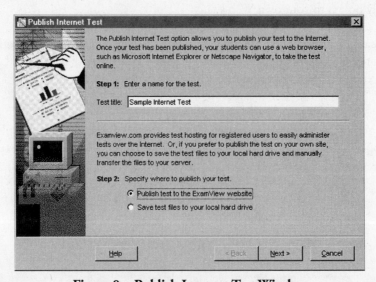

Figure 8 – Publish Internet Test Window

Step 4

Name the test.

Step 5

Select the option to publish your test to the *ExamView* Web site, and then click the **Next** button.

Step 6

Enter your instructor ID and password.

If you do not already have an instructor ID and password, click the *Register Now* button to launch your Web browser and go to the www.examview.com Web site. You cannot proceed until you have a valid instructor ID and password.

Step 7

Choose whether you want to publish a test or a study guide.

Step 8

Specify when students may access the test/study guide.

Step 9

Enter the expiration date.

Step 10

Specify who should have access to this test/study guide.

Anyone may take it, or you may limit access to a particular group of students. If you specify a roster, students must enter an ID and password.

Step 11

Enter a student password, and click **Next**.

Step 12

Review the summary information. Click the **Back** button if you need to make changes. (See Figure 9.)

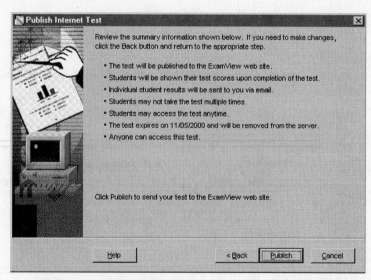

Figure 9 – Publish Internet Test Window (Summary)

Step 13

Click the **Publish** button when you are ready to post the test/study guide to the *ExamView* Web site.

The program automatically connects to the Internet and posts the test/study guide to the *ExamView* server. Access the instructor options on the *ExamView* Web site (www.examview.com) to preview a test, change selected parameters, or view results. If you need to edit or delete questions, you must change the test locally and then publish a new version. **Note:** An Internet connection is required to publish a test/study guide.

Step 14

Print a copy of the test/study guide for your records, create another test, or exit the software if you are finished.

Take a Test/Study Guide Online at www.evtestcenter.com

Once you publish a test/study guide to the *ExamView* server, anyone in the world can access it if you provide him or her with your instructor ID and the appropriate password. (**IMPORTANT:** *Do **not** give students your password, just your ID.*) Provide the instructions below to your students so that they can take the test or study guide.

Note: You must use a browser such as Netscape 4.0/Internet Explorer 4.0 (or a more recent version) that supports cascading style sheets level 1 (CSS1) and JavaScript. An active Internet connection is also required.

To take a test:

Step 1

Start your Web browser.

Step 2

Go to the URL: www.evtestcenter.com.

Step 3

Enter your instructor's ID code. (See Figure 10.)

Upon entering a valid instructor code, you will see a list of tests your instructor has published.

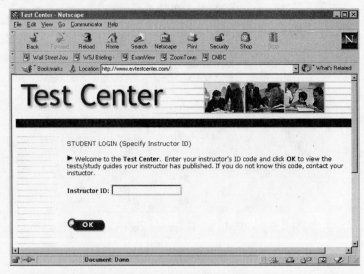

Figure 10 – Test Center Login (www.evtestcenter.com)

Step 4

Select a test.

Step 5

Enter your name (if requested), student ID, and password.

Contact your instructor if you have not been assigned a student ID or you do not have a password.

Step 6

Review the test and respond to all of the questions. (See the sample test in Figure 11.)

If you need help while working with a test, click the **Help** button shown at the bottom of the test. Click the browser's **Back** button to return to the test.

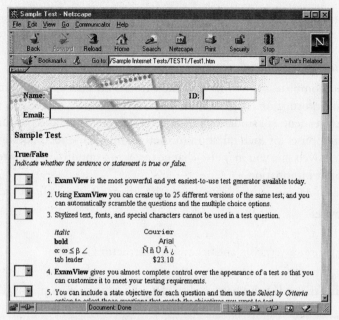

Figure 11 – Sample Internet Test

Step 7

When you complete the test, review the entire test and then click the **Grade & Submit** button located at the bottom of the test.

Your results will be emailed to your instructor. Depending on the test settings, you may be notified of your results immediately.

To complete a study guide:

Step 1

Start your Web browser.

Step 2

Go to the URL: www.evtestcenter.com.

Step 3

Enter your instructor's ID.

You will see a list of study guides and tests your instructor has published.

Step 4

Select a study guide.

Step 5

Enter your name (if requested), student ID, and password.

Contact your instructor if you have not been assigned a student ID or you do not have a password.

Step 6

Review the study guide and answer all of the questions.

If you need help while working with a study guide, click the Help button shown at the bottom of the screen. Click the browser's Back button to return to the study guide.

Step 7

When you complete the study guide, review your responses and then click the **Check Your Work** button located at the bottom of the study guide.

Your work is scored and you will see whether you answered each question correctly or incorrectly. No results are sent to your instructor.

Step 8

Click the **Reset** button to erase all of your responses if you want to start over.

Review Student Results and Manage Tests

When your students complete an Internet test, their results are automatically stored on the server so that you can easily access this information. If you chose to receive results via email, you will also receive the following information for each student: (1) student name and ID, (2) raw score and percentage score for objective-based questions, and (3) responses for each question (objective and open-ended questions).

At the *ExamView* Web site, you may also change test-setup options, preview tests, download student results, and view your account information.

Step 1

Start your Web browser.

Step 2

Go to the URL: www.examview.com and access the Instructor Center.

Step 3

Log in using your instructor ID and password to view the main menu options. (See Figure 12.)

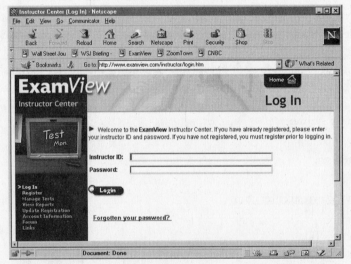

Figure 12 – ExamView Web Site (Instructor Center)

PUBLISHING TESTS TO YOUR OWN WEB SITE

If you choose not to sign up for the *ExamView* test-hosting service, you can still publish tests/study guides to your own Web site. You must save the test/study guide to your hard drive, upload the files to your Web site, and then provide access to your students. Refer to the following sections for step-by-step instructions.

Save an Internet Test/Study Guide to Your Hard Drive

Follow the steps shown below to create an Internet test/study guide and save it your hard drive. Before you begin, make sure that you installed the *ExamView* test generator software.

Step 1

Start the ExamView software.

Step 2

Create a new test or open an existing test.

Select the questions you want to include on the test. You can include any of the twelve (12) question types on a test, but only the objective questions will be graded.

Step 3

Select the *Publish Internet Test* option from the **File** menu.

ExamView presents a window with various Internet testing options to help you prepare the online test. (See Figure 13.) **Note:** Click the **Help** button if you need more assistance.

Step 4

Name the test.

Step 5

Select the option to save the test files to your local hard drive, and then click the **Next** button.

Step 6

Choose whether you want to publish a test or a study guide.

Step 7

Review the summary information. Make changes, if necessary.

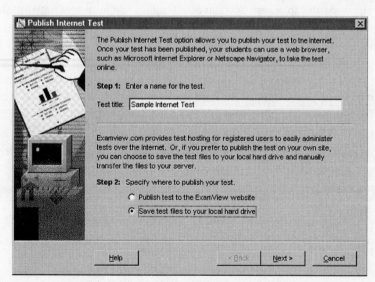

Figure 13 – Publish Internet Test Window

Step 8

Click the Save button to save the test/study guide files.

When you choose to save an Internet test to your local hard drive, *ExamView* creates an HTML file and an accompanying folder with all of the necessary image files. This makes it easier for you to post the files to a Web server. If, for example, you enter a path such as **c:\examview\tests\chapter1** (Windows) or **HD:ExamView:Tests:Chapter1** (Macintosh), the software will create a file called **chapter1.htm** and a new folder called **chapter1_files** with all of the required picture files. (See the illustration below.)

Step 9

Post the test/study guide to a server to make it available to your students. (See the next section for instructions for posting a test to a server.)

Step 10

Once you post a test, you should verify that students can access it. You may also want to try the "Grade & Submit" feature for tests to make sure that the results are emailed to the correct address.

Note: When you create a test, *ExamView* encrypts the answer information so that a student cannot see the answers in the HTML page source. While this does help to prevent cheating, there is no foolproof method in an unsupervised environment.

Post a Test to your own Internet/Intranet Server

Once you save a test/study guide formatted for the Internet, you must post all of the related files to a location on a server that your students can access. You can post the files to a local area network, Intranet server, or an Internet server. You **must** have an Internet connection for students to be able to submit test results. (This is not required for a study guide.)

Note: Posting to a server can be a complex process. The specific steps will vary depending on the hardware and software configuration of your server. If you are not familiar with the required steps, contact your network administrator for assistance.

Step 1

Start an FTP program or other utility that allows you to copy files from your hard drive to an Internet/Intranet server.

Step 2

Log in to your server.

Step 3

Create a new folder on your server to hold the test/study guide files.

Step 4

Copy the **HTML** file and the accompanying folder to a location on your server that your students can access.

When you choose to save an Internet test to your hard drive, **ExamView** creates an HTML file and an accompanying folder with all of the necessary image files. This makes it easier for you to post the files to a Web server.

IMPORTANT: By default, all of the file names are lowercase. Do not change the case since these files are referenced in the HTML document. You *must* copy the HTML file and the accompanying folder as is. Do not copy the HTML file into the corresponding folder. (See the illustration below.)

Step 5

Log off the server, if necessary.

Step 6

Record the URL for the test/study guide HTML document or set up a link to the test.

Take a Test or Study Guide Using the Internet

Once you post a test on a server, anyone in the world can access the test if you provide him or her with the Web (URL) address. Follow the instructions provided below to take a test or study guide.

Note: You must use a browser such as Netscape 4.0/Internet Explorer 4.0 (or a more recent version) that supports cascading style sheets level 1 (CSS1) and JavaScript. An active Internet connection is required to submit test results.

To take a test via the Internet:

Step 1

Start your Web browser.

Step 2

Type the Web address (URL) and test name (e.g., **www.school.edu\economics\test1.htm**), or enter an address for a page with a link to the test. (See the sample test in Figure 14.)

If the test is located on a local area network, use the open page command in the browser to open the test.

Step 3

Enter your name, student ID, and email address (optional).

Step 4

Answer all of the questions.

If you need help while working with a test, click the **Help** button shown at the bottom of the test. Click the browser's **Back** button to return to the test.

Step 5

When you complete the test, review your responses and then click the **Grade & Submit** button located at the bottom of the screen.

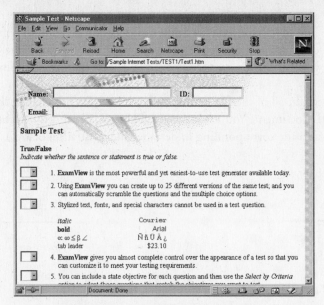

Figure 14 – Sample Internet Test

To complete a study guide via the Internet:

Step 1
Start your Web browser.

Step 2
Type the Web address (URL) and study guide name (e.g., **www.school.edu\history\study.htm**), or enter an address for a page with a link to the study guide.

Step 3
Enter your name.

Step 4
Answer all of the questions.

Step 5
When you complete the study guide, review the entire test and then click the **Check Your Work** button located at the bottom of the study guide.

Your work is scored and you will see whether you answered each question correctly or incorrectly. No results are sent to your instructor.

Step 6
Click the **Reset** button to erase all of your responses if you want to start over.

Receive Student Results via E-mail

When your students complete an Internet test, the browser sends the students' test results and all of their responses directly to you via e-mail. The e-mail will include the following information:

- student name and ID
- raw score and percentage score for objective-based questions
- responses for each question (objective and open-ended questions)

Note: **You will not receive any student results for Internet study guides.**